Raintree Steck-Vaughn

Illustrated SCIENCE ENCYCLOPEDIA

Volume
18

RES – SHR

RAINTREE
STECK-VAUGHN
PUBLISHERS
The Steck-Vaughn Company

Austin, Texas

Published by Raintree Steck-Vaughn Publishers, an imprint of Steck-Vaughn Company.

Executive Editor Diane Sharpe
Senior Editor Anne Souby
Design Manager Joyce Spicer

This edition edited and designed by Andromeda Oxford Ltd.

Andromeda Editorial and Design
Project Manager Julia Roles
Editorial Manager Jenny Fry
Design TT Designs, T&S Truscott
Cover Design John Barker

Library of Congress Cataloging-in-Publication Data
Raintree Steck-Vaughn illustrated science encyclopedia.
p. cm.
Includes bibliographical references and index.
Summary: A twenty-four volume set containing brief articles on science topics.
ISBN 0-8172-3943-X (set)
ISBN 0-8172-3936-7 (Volume 18)
1. Science—Encyclopedias, Juvenile. [1. Science—Encyclopedias.] I. Raintree Steck-Vaughn Publishers.
Q121.R354 1997
503—dc20 96-11078
CIP
AC

Printed and Bound in the United States of America.
1 2 3 4 5 6 7 8 9 10 IP 00 99 98 97 96

USING THE RAINTREE STECK-VAUGHN ILLUSTRATED SCIENCE ENCYCLOPEDIA

You are living in a world in which science, technology, and nature are very important. You see something about science almost every day. It might be on television, in the newspaper, in a book at school, or some other place. Often, you want more information about what you see.

The *Raintree Steck-Vaughn Illustrated Science Encyclopedia* will help you find what you want to know. It contains information on many science subjects. You may want to find out about computers, the environment, space exploration, biology, agriculture, or mathematics, for example. They are all in the *Raintree Steck-Vaughn Illustrated Science Encyclopedia.* There are many, many other subjects covered as well.

There are twenty-four volumes in the encyclopedia. The articles, which are called entries, are in alphabetical order through the first twenty-two volumes. On the spine of each volume, below the volume number, are some letters. The letters above the line are the first three letters of the first entry in that volume. The letters below the line are the first three letters of the last entry in that volume. In Volume 1, for example, you see that the first entry begins with **AAR** and that the last entry begins with **ANT**. Using the letters makes it easy to find the volume you need.

In Volume 23, there are three special features—reference charts and tables, a bibliography, and an index. In Volume 24, there are interesting projects that you can do on your own. The projects are fun to do, and they help you discover and understand important science principles. Many can give you ideas that can help you develop your own science fair projects.

Main Entries There are two kinds of main entries in the *Raintree Steck-Vaughn Illustrated Science Encyclopedia.* Many of the entries are major topics that are spread over several pages. The titles of these entries are shown at the top of the page in a yellow box. Other entries required less space to cover the topic fully. The titles of these main entries are printed in capital letters. They look like this: **ABALONE**. At the beginning of some entries, you will see a phonetic pronunciation of the entry title, such as (ăb′ ə lō′ nē). In the front of each volume, there is a pronunciation key. Use it the same way you use your dictionary's pronunciation key.

Cross-References Within the main entries are cross-references referring to other entries in the encyclopedia. Within an entry, they look like this: (see MAMMAL). At the end of an entry, they look like this: *See also* HYENA. These cross-references tell you where to find other helpful information on the subject you are reading about.

Projects At the end of some entries, you will see this symbol: PROJECT 1. It tells you which projects related to that entry are in Volume 24.

Illustrations There are thousands of photographs, drawings, graphs, diagrams, tables, and other illustrations in the *Raintree Steck-Vaughn Illustrated Science Encyclopedia.* They will help you better understand the entries you read. Captions describe the illustrations. Many of the illustrations also have labels that point out important parts.

Activities Some main entries include activities presented in a special box. These activities are short projects that give you a chance to work with science on your own.

Index In Volume 23, the index lists every main entry by volume and page number. Many subjects that are not main entries are also listed in the index, as well as the illustrations, projects, activities, and reference charts and tables.

Bibliography In Volume 23, there is also a bibliography for students. The books in this list are on a variety of topics and can supplement what you have learned in the *Raintree Steck-Vaughn Illustrated Science Encyclopedia.*

The *Raintree Steck-Vaughn Illustrated Science Encyclopedia* was designed especially for you, the student. It is a source of knowledge for the world of science, technology, and nature. Enjoy it!

PRONUNCIATION KEY

Each symbol has the same sound as the darker letters in the sample words.

Symbol	Sample words	Symbol	Sample words	Symbol	Sample words
ə	balloon, ago	îr	deer, pier	r	root, tire
ă	map, have	j	join, germ	s	so, press
ā	day, made	k	king, ask	sh	shoot, machine
âr	care, bear	l	let, cool	t	to, stand
ä	father, car	m	man, same	th	thin, death
b	ball, rib	n	no, turn	*th*	then, this
ch	choose, nature	ng	bring, long	ŭ	up, cut
d	did, add	ŏ	odd, pot	ûr	urge, hurt
ĕ	bell, get	ō	cone, know	v	view, give
ē	sweet, easy	ô	all, saw	w	wood, glowing
f	fan, soft	oi	boy, boil	y	yes, year
g	good, big	ou	now, loud	z	zero, raise
h	hurt, ahead	o͝o	good, took	zh	leisure, vision
ĭ	rip, ill	o͞o	boot, noon	′	strong accent
ī	side, sky	p	part, scrap	′	weak accent

GUIDE TO MEASUREMENT ABBREVIATIONS

All measurements in the *Raintree Steck-Vaughn Illustrated Science Encyclopedia* are given in both the customary system and the metric system [in brackets like these]. Following are the abbreviations used for various units of measure.

Customary Units of Measure

mi. = miles	cu. yd. = cubic yards
m.p.h. = miles per hour	cu. ft. = cubic feet
yd. = yards	cu. in. = cubic inches
ft. = feet	gal. = gallons
in. = inches	pt. = pints
sq. mi. = square miles	qt. = quarts
sq. yd. = square yards	lb. = pounds
sq. ft. = square feet	oz. = ounces
sq. in. = square inches	fl. oz. = fluid ounces
cu. mi. = cubic miles	°F = degrees Fahrenheit

Metric Units of Measure

km = kilometers	cu. km = cubic kilometers
kph = kilometers per hour	cu. m = cubic meters
m = meters	cu. cm = cubic centimeters
cm = centimeters	ml = milliliters
mm = millimeters	kg = kilograms
sq. km = square kilometers	g = grams
sq. m = square meters	mg = milligrams
sq. cm = square centimeters	°C = degrees Celsius

For information on how to convert customary measurements to metric measurements, see the Metric Conversions table in Volume 23.

RESPIRATORY SYSTEM

Most living organisms change energy that is locked in molecules of digested food into a form that can be used by the cells. This changing is done in a complex process called respiration (see METABOLISM; RESPIRATION). In order to do this, these organisms need a way to get oxygen from the air. They must also be able to put carbon dioxide, a waste product of respiration, back into the air. This part of respiration—taking in oxygen and giving off carbon dioxide—is called external respiration. In human beings and other animals, it is also called breathing. The human respiratory system (rĕs′pər ə tôr′ē sĭs′təm) is responsible for carrying out the breathing process (see BREATHING).

Human beings breathe in and out through the nose and mouth. When air enters the nose, it is warmed and moistened before it enters the lungs (see NOSE). In addition, the nose helps remove small particles of dirt and dust. The nose and mouth are joined in the back of the mouth in an area called the pharynx. A tube called the trachea, or windpipe, also opens into the pharynx (see TRACHEA). At the top of the trachea is the larynx, or voice box (see LARYNX). The larynx contains the vocal cords, which vibrate to make sound. The trachea is next to and in front of a tube called the esophagus. The esophagus leads to the stomach. There is a flap of skin-covered cartilage, called the epiglottis, located at the top of the larynx (see CARTILAGE). When a person eats or drinks, muscles in the neck pull the epiglottis and trachea together, sealing the trachea so that the food or liquid cannot accidentally enter it. Sometimes, however, food or liquid may enter the trachea by mistake. This causes the person to cough in an attempt to clear the foreign material out of the trachea.

As it nears the top of the chest, the trachea divides into two smaller tubes, each of which is called a bronchus. Each bronchus splits into several smaller tubes called bronchioles. The trachea, bronchi (plural of *bronchus*), and bronchioles all have rings of cartilage that keep them open. They are also lined with cilia (plural of *cilium*), which trap tiny particles of dust or dirt in the air (see CILIUM). The bronchioles divide into smaller and smaller tubes and eventually end in clusters of alveoli, which are round air sacs (see LUNG). Each lung has millions of alveoli. The alveoli have thin walls that contain many capillaries (tiny blood vessels).

There are two lungs, both of which lie in the airtight thoracic cavity (chest). The lungs are contained in a thin, tough membrane called the pleura. The thoracic cavity is protected by the ribs and the muscles between the ribs, which are called the intercostal muscles. At the bottom of the thoracic cavity, below the lungs, is a powerful, dome-shaped muscle called the diaphragm (see DIAPHRAGM).

A person's breathing is automatically controlled by the respiratory center in the brain. This center is chiefly sensitive to the amount of carbon dioxide in

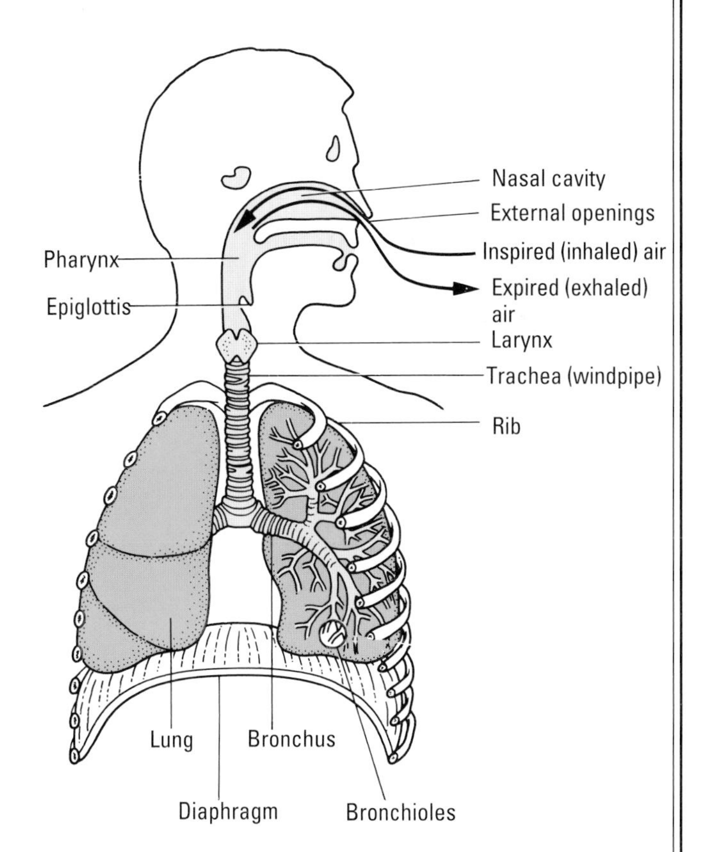

HUMAN RESPIRATORY SYSTEM

The human respiratory system extends from the nasal cavity to the diaphragm. Air entering via the nasal cavity passes to the pharynx, past the epiglottis and larynx, and into the trachea (windpipe). The epiglottis prevents food from entering the trachea. The trachea branches into two bronchi (plural of *bronchus*), which lead into the lungs and subdivide into many bronchioles.

the blood. If there is an increase in carbon dioxide, such as during strenuous exercise, the respiratory center sends more nerve signals to the muscles that control breathing. As a result, the person breathes faster. It is possible for someone to hold his or her breath, or stop breathing, for a while. After a short time, however, the person can no longer do so, and the automatic breathing starts again. The respiratory center in the brain also responds to the amount of oxygen in the blood. In addition, the rate of breathing is influenced by adrenaline, a hormone from the adrenal glands (see ADRENAL GLANDS).

Breathing has two parts: inspiration (inhaling, or breathing in), and expiration (exhaling, or breathing out). When a person inhales, his or her chest expands, and the lungs fill with air. To do this, the diaphragm contracts and moves downward. At the same time, the muscles between the ribs also contract, moving the rib cage upward and outward. After inhaling, there is a short pause before exhaling begins. When a person exhales, the diaphragm and rib muscles relax, the chest becomes smaller, and air is forced out of the lungs.

With each normal breath, a person changes about 10 to 15 percent of the air in his or her lungs. When resting, an adult inhales or exhales about 0.5 qt. [0.5 liter] with each breath. This is called the tidal capacity. During heavy breathing, a person may exchange about 4.75 qt. [4.5 liters] of air with each breath. This is called the vital capacity. There is at least 1.5 qt. [1.4 liters] of air in the lungs at all times. This is called the residual capacity. The total lung capacity of an adult man is about 6.4 qt. [6 liters]. It is usually less in women and more in trained athletes.

When a person inhales, air fills the alveoli. The capillaries in the alveoli are so tiny that red blood cells have to go through one at a time. Oxygen diffuses through the thin capillary walls and combines with hemoglobin in the red blood cells (see BLOOD; HEMOGLOBIN). The oxygen-rich blood then flows back to the heart, which pumps it throughout the body. In the tissues, the blood once again enters tiny capillaries. Here, the oxygen is freed from the hemoglobin. The oxygen then diffuses into the tissues and cells. Carbon dioxide diffuses out of the cells and tissues into the capillaries. Most of the carbon dioxide is dissolved in the watery plasma of the blood. When the blood returns to the lungs, the carbon dioxide is released and is exhaled. The whole process repeats itself every few seconds.

See also CIRCULATORY SYSTEM; DIFFUSION.

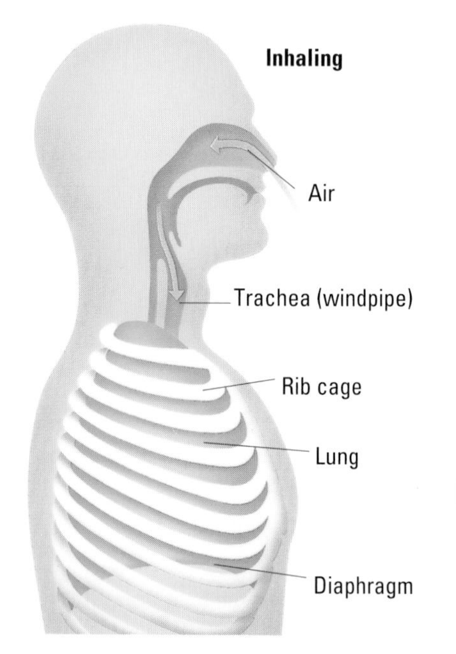

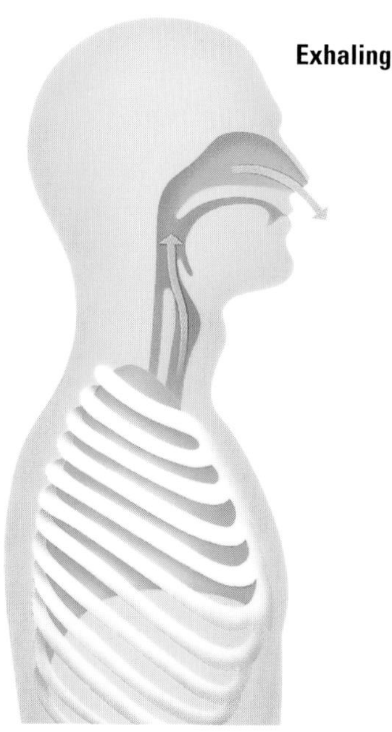

BREATHING

Inhaling (inspiration) and exhaling (expiration) take place when a person breathes. During inhaling, the chest expands, and the lungs fill with air. To do this, the diaphragm contracts and moves downward. At the same time, the rib cage moves upward and outward. During exhaling, the diaphragm and rib muscles relax, the chest becomes smaller, and air is forced out of the lungs.

REVERSIBLE REACTION In chemistry, a reversible reaction is one that can proceed in either direction. The reaction of sulfur dioxide and oxygen to make sulfur trioxide is a reversible reaction used in the manufacture of sulfuric acid.

$$2SO_2 + O_2 \rightleftharpoons 2SO_3$$

All three substances are present in the reaction mixture. The fact that the reaction is reversible is shown by the double arrows. The direction in which a reaction proceeds depends on the temperature, pressure, and concentration of the substances. At a particular temperature, pressure, and concentration of substances, the reaction is in equilibrium—that is, both forward and reverse reactions proceed at the same rate—and the amounts of each substance in the reaction remain constant.
See also CHEMICAL FORMULAS AND EQUATIONS; EQUILIBRIUM.

REVOLUTION A revolution is a movement that takes an object round in a circular (or near-circular) path so that it returns to its starting point. The earth and other planets revolve around the sun. The earth takes one year to complete one revolution around the sun. A spinning object, such as a spinning top, revolves around a line or axis. Each part of the top follows a circular path around the axis as the top spins. The parts complete one revolution for each turn of the top.
See also ORBIT.

RHESUS FACTOR The Rhesus factor, or Rh factor, is a protein found on the walls of red blood cells (see BLOOD). It is named after the rhesus monkeys in which it was first detected. There are at least 33 different types of these proteins, which are types of antigen. People are described as being either Rh-positive (where the Rh factor is present) or Rh-negative (where it is not). However, only one of the Rh antigens is important. It causes a very strong immune reaction if it is introduced into a Rh-negative person's bloodstream (see IMMUNITY). This is most likely to happen when a woman gives birth, if the baby is Rh-positive and the mother is Rh-negative. If subsequent babies are also Rh-positive, the antibodies in the mother's blood formed after the first exposure can harm the baby, causing destruction of the red blood cells and leading to anemia, brain damage, and even death (see ANEMIA; ANTIBODY). Because of this risk, Rh-negative mothers are given doses of the Rh antibody after the first child is born. This stops the reaction.
See also BLOOD TYPE.

RHEUMATIC FEVER (ro͞o măt′ĭk fē′vər) Rheumatic fever is a serious infectious disease that attacks the joints and the hearts of children and young adults. Doctors believe that the disease occurs as a result of previous infection by a group of bacteria called group A *Streptococci* (see BACTERIA). However, no one knows exactly how this group of *Streptococci* attacks the body to cause rheumatic fever.

The usual symptoms of rheumatic fever are fever, rash, and inflammation and pain in the joints (see INFLAMMATION). The tissues of the heart become inflamed. If the heart is badly affected, there are symptoms of heart failure.

Rheumatic fever is one of the greatest causes of heart disease in young people, though some people recover fully without heart damage. In others, the disease seriously affects the valves of the heart. The results of the damage may not show up for years (see HEART DISEASE).

Rheumatic fever can be prevented by prompt antibiotic treatment of group A *Streptococci* infections of the pharynx, commonly called strep throat (see ANTIBIOTIC; RESPIRATORY SYSTEM; STREP THROAT). Once rheumatic fever has developed, a doctor will order complete bed rest until all symptoms of fever and inflammation are gone. Drugs such as aspirin are often used to relieve pain. Hormones may also be given to reduce inflammation.
See also ASPIRIN; HORMONE.

RHINOCEROS (rī nŏs′ər əs) The rhinoceros is one of the largest land animals. This mammal's large body is carried by short, stout legs (see MAMMAL). Most rhinoceroses have very little hair and very thick skin. The skin hangs loosely from the body. The name *rhinoceros* comes from two Greek words, *rhino,* meaning "nose," and *keros,* meaning "horned." The animals have one or two curved horns that stick out from the long snout. The horns grow throughout the animal's life.

The rhinoceros belongs to the "odd-toed" group of hoofed mammals, or ungulates (see UNGULATE). The animal has three toes on each foot, each toe ending in a separate hoof. Each front foot also has a fourth toe that is not used.

Rhinoceroses in the wild feed on grass, twigs, and shrubs. In captivity, such as in zoos, the animals are fed hay and diet supplements.

There are five species of rhinoceroses. Three species live in Asia and two in Africa. All the species, especially the Asian ones, have been hunted nearly to extinction and are now protected by law (see ENDANGERED SPECIES; EXTINCTION).

The Indian rhinoceros is the largest of the Asian rhinoceroses. It stands up to 6 ft. 4 in. [1.9 m] at the shoulder and weighs up to 2 tons [1.8 metric tons]. It has one bluish black horn. The Indian rhinoceros lives in marshy jungles, among reeds and tall grass. Another Asian rhinoceros, the Javan rhinoceros, is nearly extinct. The third Asian rhinoceros, the Sumatran, has two short horns. It is the smallest of all the species of rhinoceros, weighing no more than 1 ton [0.9 metric ton].

Both African species are two horned. The black rhinoceros, also called the hook-lipped rhinoceros, is bluish gray in color. The animal's front horn, which may be 3.5 ft. [107 cm] in length, is used for defense. This rhinoceros lives on dry plains covered with brush. The white rhinoceros, also colored bluish gray, is the largest of all rhinoceroses. Square-lipped rhinoceros is another name for this species. Some white rhinoceroses are more than 6 ft. [1.8 m] in height and weigh about 3.5 tons [3.2 metric tons].

RHINOCEROS

Shown here are three of the five species of rhinoceros. (1) The white rhinoceros and (2) the black rhinoceros come from Africa. Both have two horns. (3) The one-horned Indian rhinoceros lives in India and Nepal. All species of rhinoceros are now rare.

RHIZOME (rī′zōm′) A rhizome is an underground stem that often looks and acts like a root (see ROOT; STEM). It is different from a root, however, because it has buds and it usually grows horizontally (see BUD). Rhizomes usually produce aerial (above-ground) stems and underground roots from these buds. Some rhizomes become swollen with a supply of stored food (see TUBER). Plants that have rhizomes include gingers, some irises, and some ferns.
See also VEGETATIVE PROPAGATION.

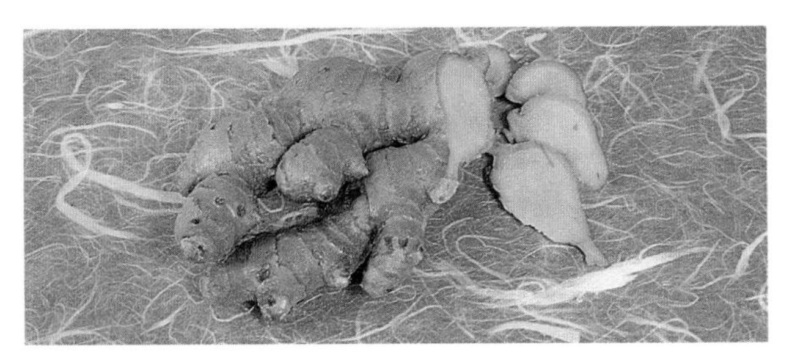

RHIZOME
A rhizome is a swollen underground plant stem. The rhizomes pictured are from a ginger plant.

RHODODENDRON (rō′də dĕn′drən) A rhododendron is a small tree or large shrub that belongs to the heath family, Ericaceae. It is related to the azalea and mountain laurel (see HEATH FAMILY). There are hundreds of species of rhododendron throughout the world, especially in the Himalayas and eastern Asia. Several live naturally in North America, in the mountainous areas of the eastern United States and Canada. These rhododendrons are evergreen, with showy white, pink, or purple flowers (see EVERGREEN). Rhododendrons are often cultivated as ornamental plants in parks and lawns.

RHODODENDRON
Rhododendrons are grown for their large, showy flowers. In many places they also grow wild.

RHUBARB (ro͞o′bärb′) Rhubarb is a plant that belongs to the buckwheat family (see BUCKWHEAT FAMILY). It is one of the few perennial vegetables (see PERENNIAL PLANT). Rhubarb has a large, yellow storage root. In spring, the plant sends up large glossy leaves, up to 2 ft. [60 cm] wide. The leaves have long, fleshy stalks that grow as tall as 2 ft. [60 cm] and as thick as 1 in. [2.5 cm]. These stalks are the edible parts of the plant, but the green leaf blades are poisonous. A large, central flower stalk bears clusters of small, greenish flowers.

The rhubarb stalks have a small amount of vitamin C. They also act as a mild laxative (see LAXATIVE). They are used mainly in pies and other desserts.

RHUBARB
If allowed to go to seed, rhubarb plants produce a large flower stalk bearing clusters of small, greenish flowers.

RIB In human beings, the ribs are twelve pairs of thin, curved bones that enclose the thoracic cavity (chest). They are attached to the vertebrae of the backbone in the back, and circle around toward the front of the body (see VERTEBRA). The first seven pairs are attached by cartilage to the sternum (breastbone) in front (see CARTILAGE). They are called the true ribs. The next five pairs are called the false ribs. Each of the upper three false ribs is attached to the rib above by cartilage. The bottom two pairs of false ribs are shorter than the others, reaching only about halfway around. In other words, they are attached only to the backbone. These are called the floating ribs. The spaces between the ribs (called the intercostal spaces) are filled with muscles, blood vessels, and nerves. The ribs protect the heart and lungs. They also help with the breathing process (see RESPIRATORY SYSTEM).

Most vertebrates (animals with backbones) have ribs. Ribs first evolved in the fishes. Fishes have two sets of ribs, neither of which is joined in front. Reptiles are the lowest animals with ribs joined in front. In snakes, each vertebra of the body gives rise to a pair of ribs. In mammals, however, only the thoracic vertebrae have ribs. The other vertebrae have small bony stumps that are vestiges of ribs lost during evolution (see VESTIGIAL ORGAN). The number of ribs in mammals varies from nine pairs in whales to twenty-four pairs in the two-toed sloth.

See also BONE; EVOLUTION; SKELETON.

RIBOSOME (rī′bə sōm) Ribosomes are small organelles in a cell. In most cells, ribosomes are attached to the endoplasmic reticulum, a network of canallike passages between the cell membrane and the cell nucleus. In some cells, however, ribosomes are attached to the cell membrane. Proteins are made on the ribosomes (see PROTEIN). Ribosomes contain a type of RNA called ribosomal RNA (rRNA).

See also CELL; CYTOPLASM; ORGANELLE; RNA.

RICE Rice is an edible cereal crop that belongs to the grass family (see CEREAL CROP; GRASS). This annual plant produces shoots that are about 3.3 ft. [1 m] tall (see ANNUAL PLANT). Each shoot carries fifty to three hundred spikelets in a drooping head (see INFLORESCENCE). Each spikelet produces a grain of rice. The grain has a brown skin called a bran coat. Outside this is a tough husk.

RICE—New varieties

New varieties of rice are grown at a plant-breeding station. Bags over the flowers prevent cross-pollination.

More than half the people in the world rely on rice as their major food. Rice is about 80 percent carbohydrate, 12 percent water, and 8 percent protein. The bran coat is rich in the vitamins thiamine, niacin, and riboflavin (see CARBOHYDRATE; PROTEIN; VITAMIN). Sometimes, this bran coat is removed during milling. Milling is the process that removes the husk. Rice with the brancoat removed is white and is called polished rice. A person whose diet consists chiefly of polished rice may suffer from a deficiency disease (see BERIBERI; DEFICIENCY DISEASES). Brown rice still has its bran coat and is more nutritious than polished rice. Rice is sometimes steamed under pressure before it is milled. This softens the kernels and allows the vitamins and minerals to spread through them, so they are not lost during milling. Rice treated in this way is called parboiled rice. Enriched rice has added vitamins and iron (see FOOD PROCESSING). Both parboiled and enriched rice are white.

There are about twenty species of rice, but only two—Asian rice and African rice—are cultivated. There are thousands of different varieties, each suited to a particular area. Most rice is grown in flooded fields or marshes in tropical and subtropical areas. Several varieties, called upland rice, are grown on dry land. More than 90 percent of the world's rice is grown in Asia. Even this is not enough to feed the Asian people. Only about 1 percent of the world's rice supply comes from the

RICE—Planting and harvesting

Most rice is grown in flooded fields called paddies (top). Rice grows rapidly and needs little attention while it is growing (center). In many southeast Asian countries, rice is still harvested by hand (bottom). Rice grown on dry land may be harvested using machines.

United States, and about half of this is exported. The leading rice-growing states are Arkansas, California, Louisiana, and Texas. In addition to its use as a food, rice can be made into beer or into a wine called saki.

RICHTER SCALE (rĭk′tər skāl) The Richter scale is a system of measuring the strength (energy) of earthquakes. It was devised in 1935 by the American seismologist Charles F. Richter (see EARTHQUAKE; MERCALLI SCALE; SEISMOLOGY). The Richter scale starts at zero and has no upper limit. The weakest earth tremors (vibrations) have a Richter scale reading close to zero. The strongest earthquake measured on the Richter scale had a strength of 8.9. It has been calculated that the San Francisco earthquake of 1906 would have measured 8.3 on the Richter scale.

Richter scale measurements are calculated by scientists using data from a seismograph. A seismograph is an instrument that records vibrations of the earth's crust. Each number on the Richter scale represents an earthquake ten times stronger and releasing thirty-one times the energy than the previous number. Thus, an earthquake that measures 5 on the Richter scale is ten times stronger than an earthquake that measures 4.

Scientists estimate that more than a thousand earthquakes occur daily that measure less than 2 on the Richter scale. Such earthquakes cause little or no damage. Earthquakes that measure 7 or more on the Richter scale cause widespread damage, injuries, and deaths.

RICKETS Rickets is a disease occurring mainly in children in which the bones do not grow properly. It is usually caused by a lack of vitamin D in the diet (see DEFICIENCY DISEASES; DIET). Vitamin D plays an important role in the intake of calcium by the bone tissue, and without it the bones become soft and eventually bend (see BONE). Rickets is treated by ensuring that the child gets enough vitamin D and enough exposure to sunlight (which changes the vitamin into a form that the body can use). A healthy diet will contain enough vitamin D.

A rare form of rickets is caused not by poor diet, but by a genetic disease called familial hypophosphatemia. The child carries a gene that causes his or her body to excrete too much calcium salt from the kidneys (see DIALYSIS; GENE). This in turn causes a loss of calcium from the bones, and rickets develops. The treatment is to give massive doses of vitamin D and calcium in the diet. One day, it may be possible to treat the disease with genetic engineering techniques (see GENETIC ENGINEERING; GENETICS).

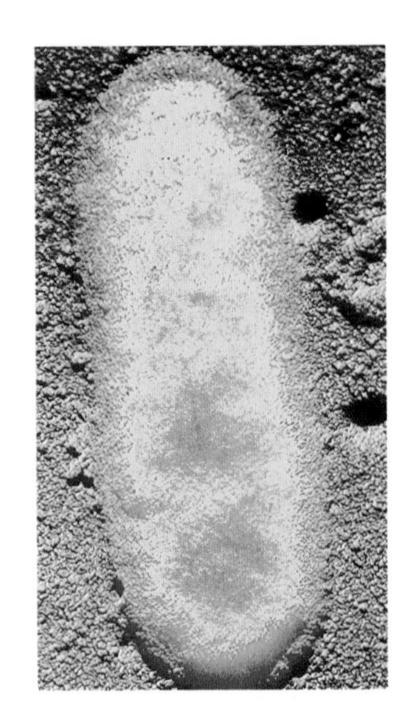

RICKETTSIA

Rickettsias are a group of rod-shaped bacteria. They can cause a number of serious diseases in humans and other mammals. These diseases include typhus and Rocky Mountain spotted fever.

RICKETTSIA (rĭ kĕt'sē ə) Rickettsias are a group of disease-producing microorganisms. They are usually regarded as a special kind of bacteria (see MICROORGANISM; PATHOGEN). Rickettsias usually enter the bloodstream of human beings by the bite of fleas, ticks, or lice. When introduced into a person's bloodstream, rickettsias can cause a number of diseases, such as Rocky Mountain spotted fever, trench fever, and typhus (see DISEASE; INFECTION; TYPHUS).

Like viruses, rickettsias cannot survive outside of living cells (see VIRUS). Unlike viruses, rickettsias can be killed with certain antibiotics or sulfa drugs (see ANTIBIOTIC; SULFA DRUG). Rickettsias are named for Howard Taylor Ricketts, an American scientist who studied them. Ricketts died as a result of rickettsial infection.

RIFT VALLEY A rift valley is a sunken area of land along a fault. It was once thought that a rift valley was formed by a block subsiding, or sinking down, between two parallel faults. Now scientists have found that only one wall at such a valley is

RIFT VALLEY

The Great Rift Valley, pictured here, is the longest rift valley in the world. It runs along eastern Africa from Mozambique, in the south, to the Red Sea, in the north.

formed by a fault. The other wall is formed by the earth's crust bending downward (see FAULT).

Rift valleys are numerous in the southwestern United States. Death Valley is a well-known example of a rift valley. The longest rift valley on land is the Great Rift Valley in eastern Africa. It runs from Mozambique through Ethiopia to Eritrea, with a northern extension that includes the Red Sea. Great rift valleys also occur under the oceans.

RIGHT WHALE The right whale is any of three species of baleen whales belonging to the family Balaenidae. Baleen whales do not have teeth. Instead, their mouths contain bony plates to strain small organisms out of the water. A right whale is noted for its firm, thick body and huge triangular head. The upper jaw is very curved. The lower jaw forms a scoop.

The right whale probably gets its name from the fact that two kinds—the bowhead, or Greenland right whale, and the black right whale—were long considered the "right" whales to catch by whale hunters. These large whales gave a good yield of oil and whalebone, and were relatively easy to catch. Both species have become endangered because of uncontrolled hunting. Since 1946, they have been protected by international agreement. The third kind of right whale is much smaller and is called the pygmy right whale. It lives in the Southern Hemisphere.

See also ENDANGERED SPECIES; WHALE.

RINGWORM Ringworm is the common name for several skin diseases caused by fungi (plural of *fungus*) (see FUNGUS). The name comes from the fact that the fungi may produce ring-shaped, red, scaly patches on the skin. One form of ringworm, commonly called athlete's foot, is caused by the fungus *Tinea pedis.* It causes a whiteness and scaliness between the toes that may be followed by painful blisters. *Tinea capitis* is a fungus that causes ringworm of the scalp. It is very contagious and may cause an epidemic among schoolchildren (see EPIDEMIC). The various fungi (genus *Tinea*) that cause ringworm infections usually feed on keratin (protein) in the skin (see KERATIN). They may be controlled by various fungicidal medicines sold in pharmacies.

See also DISEASE; FUNGICIDE; INFECTION.

RIGHT WHALE

The enormous head of the black right whale, also called the Biscayan whale (above), makes up more than a third of its body length. A bowhead whale (left) has a huge lower jaw that it uses to scoop up the plankton on which it feeds. The mouths of both whales contain bony plates, called baleen, that strain plankton out of large volumes of seawater.

River

A river is a large stream of water that flows over land, usually from a high area to a low area. The water comes from rain, melted snow, lakes, and springs seeping from underground. The place where a river begins is called its source. The river water eventually flows into a larger river, a lake, or the ocean. The place where this happens is called the mouth of the river. Rivers play an important part in recirculating the earth's water (see WATER CYCLE).

There are many kinds of rivers. There are fast rivers, slow rivers, straight rivers, winding rivers, large rivers, and small rivers. Rivers are smaller at the place where they begin. As they flow toward their destination, drain more land, and receive water from other streams and rivers flowing into them (called tributaries), they become larger. The Mississippi River—the largest in North America—drains nearly two-thirds of the continental United States and part of Canada. At its source in Minnesota, a person can step over the

START OF A RIVER

Many rivers start from a mountain lake or waterfall (left). The water feeds a stream, which gets bigger as it collects more water from side streams called tributaries.

RIVER SOURCE

A typical river source is pictured below. Rainwater is trapped in a layer of permeable chalk between layers of impermeable clay. (Permeable means "can be penetrated.") Along the lines where the chalk and clay layers meet, the water flows out through springs and forms streams that run down the hillside. On the left side of the hill, these streams collect in the valley to form a river.

RIVER DELTA

The Nile River delta in Egypt is the large, dark, triangular area in this picture (right), which was taken from space.

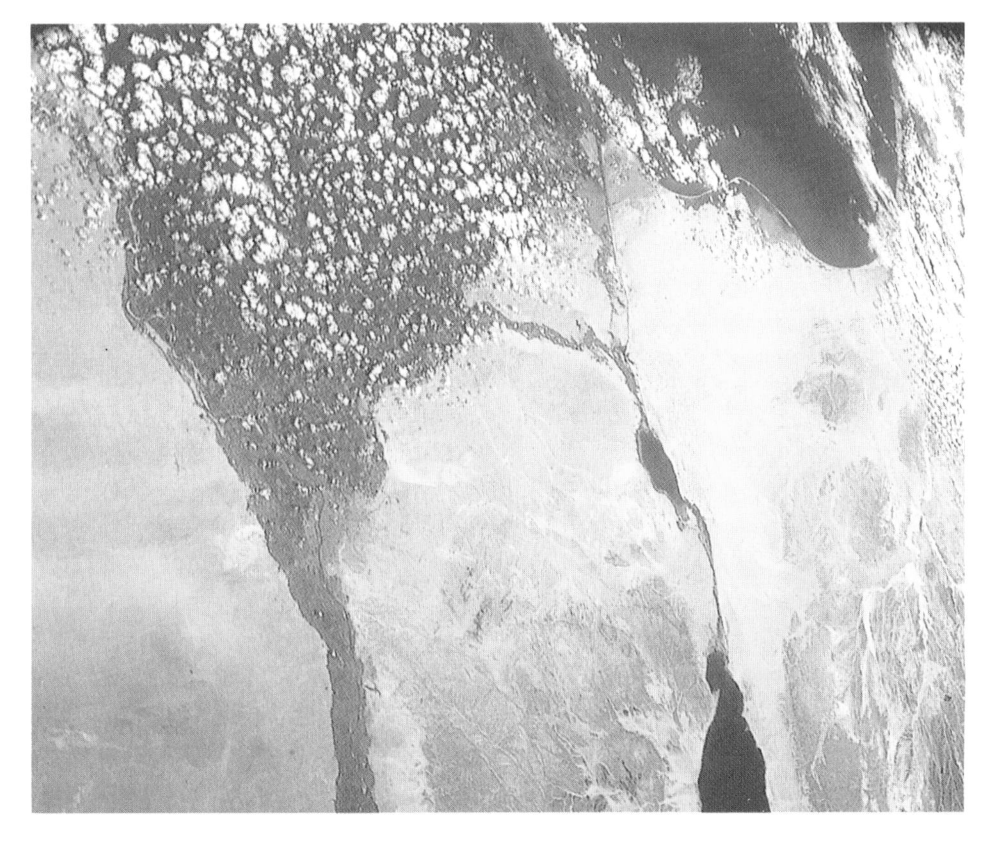

END OF A RIVER

River water carries along with it particles of mud and sand. At the mouth of the river (below) these particles may be deposited to form a fan-shaped delta.

Mississippi River. Before it empties into the Gulf of Mexico in Louisiana, it is more than a mile wide. From its source to its mouth, the Mississippi River is 2,470 mi. [3,952 km] long.

Rivers go through several stages during their existence. These are commonly called the youthful, the mature, and the old-age stages. Often, different parts of a river are in different stages. The source of the river is usually in the young stage; the middle of the river is often in the mature stage; and the mouth of the river is frequently in the old-age stage. The mouth may have a delta, an area of land formed by mud and sand that has been deposited at the mouth (see DELTA).

The youthful stage A young river has a steep slope, irregular current, steep banks (edges), and cold, clear water. The water has just begun to cut a valley in the earth (see EROSION). Young rivers have many waterfalls and rapids (see WATERFALL AND RAPID). Trout and a few minnows live in the water.

YOUNG RIVER
The Yellowstone River in Wyoming is in its youthful stage. The fast-flowing water pours over many waterfalls and rapids. The river is world famous for the trout fishing it provides.

The mature stage At the mature stage, a river flattens out, and its valley widens. There are few waterfalls and rapids. The water warms and becomes less clear due to algae and dirt (see ALGAE). The river often flows in wide bends, called meanders. Bass, sunfish, perch, and many species of minnows live in the water.

The old-age stage Old rivers flow over a nearly level plain. The valley is very wide, and the water is usually muddy from washing against the banks and carrying soil from upstream. Because of the low banks, the river often overflows its banks and floods the surrounding countryside. The floods spread the soil that is carried in the water across the ground. This soil is very rich and good for growing crops. Catfish, carp, bass, eels, and many species of minnows live in the water.

Today, many geographers dislike the youthful, mature, and old-age divisions. This is because these divisions suggest that the current is faster in the early stage than in the later. In fact, it is now known that the current is usually faster when the river is flowing over a flat plain, because there are no bumps and outcrops to slow it down.

Importance of rivers Rivers have been very important in the development of civilization. The earliest civilizations began along rivers of Asia, Africa, and the Middle East. People first learned to

Key

New deposits

Older deposits

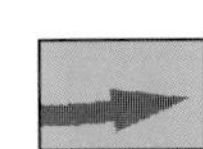
River channel and strongest currents

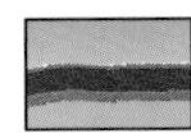
Riverbanks being eroded

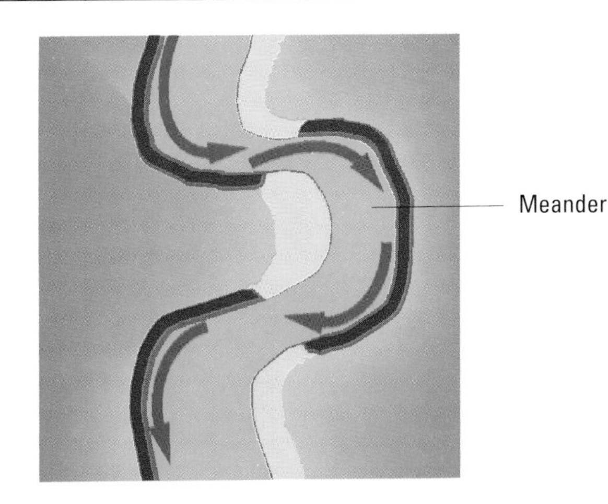

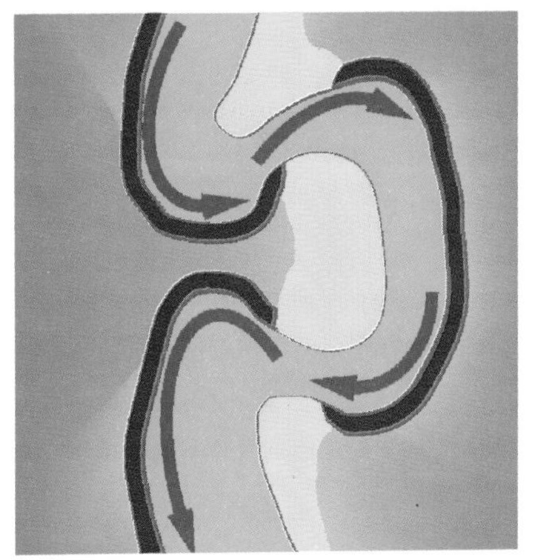

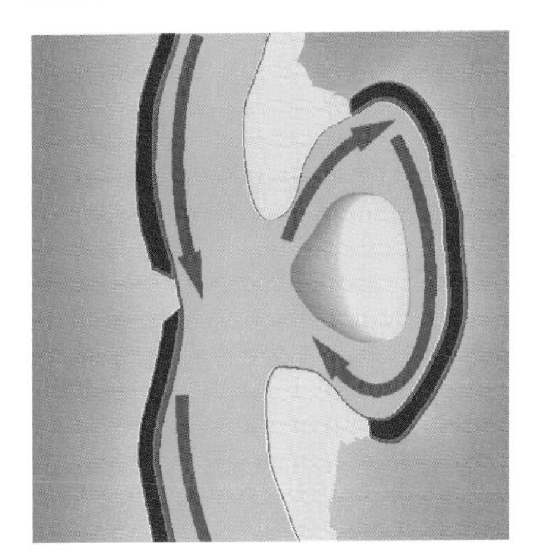

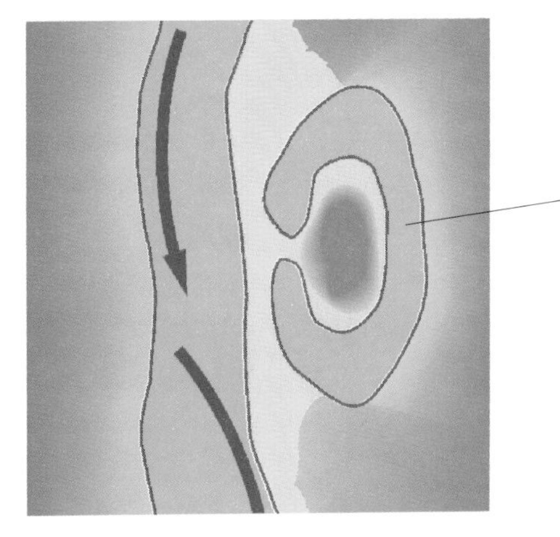

MEANDERS AND OXBOW LAKES

Before a river (below) reaches its mouth, it usually crosses a plain and often forms meanders (bends) and so-called oxbow lakes (cut-off bends). The four illustrations at right show the stages in the formation of an oxbow lake from a meander.

raise crops and irrigate near rivers (see IRRIGATION). Rivers have always supplied people with food, water, and transportation.

During the Industrial Revolution, factories and mills were built along rivers because the current could power the machinery, goods could be moved in and out by boat, and wastes could be dumped into the river.

Today, many rivers are so polluted that they cannot be used for drinking and some other purposes (see POLLUTION). We now realize that we cannot dump our garbage into rivers if we want to drink the water; eat the fish; or safely swim, ski, and boat on the rivers. Governments and industry are trying to clean up badly polluted rivers.

RNA The initials *RNA* stand for *ribonucleic acid.* RNA, found in the cells of living organisms and in some viruses, is a complex chemical compound that plays an important role in the making of proteins. Proteins are necessary for the survival of every living organism (see CELL; COMPOUND; PROTEIN; VIRUS). RNA is a nucleic acid. A nucleic acid is made of chains of units called nucleotides. Each nucleotide in RNA contains phosphate (a salt of phosphoric acid), a sugar called ribose, and compounds called bases (see BASE). There are four kinds of bases in RNA: adenine, guanine, cytosine, and uracil (see NUCLEIC ACID).

Several "types" of RNA perform important functions in the making of proteins. Messenger RNA (mRNA) is found in the nucleus, or control center, of the cell. Transfer RNA (tRNA) is found in the cytoplasm, the watery liquid that makes up much of the cell. Another type of RNA is called ribosomal RNA (rRNA); it occurs in the ribosomes. The ribosomes are the structures within cells where protein synthesis (manufacture) occurs.

The first step in protein synthesis occurs in the cell nucleus, where DNA—another nucleic acid, which is the carrier of genetic information in cells—directs the manufacture of mRNA. The mRNA contains coded instructions needed to make a specific protein. The instructions are in the form of triplets of nucleotides, called codons. The newly formed mRNA leaves the nucleus and travels to a ribosome. There, rRNA "reads" the information coded on the mRNA. Also in the ribosome, the mRNA meets molecules of tRNA. Each tRNA molecule carries an amino acid. Amino acids are the "building blocks" of proteins (see AMINO ACID).

A sequence of three nucleotides, called an anticodon, occurs on tRNA. Certain codons on the mRNA signal the beginning of the protein synthesis process. A codon on the mRNA links with an anticodon on the tRNA. The tRNA then deposits the amino acid it is carrying. Another tRNA links up to the mRNA, and the original tRNA leaves the ribosome. The second tRNA then deposits its amino acid. This process continues until the instructions of the mRNA are completely carried out. This usually happens after thousands of amino acids have been deposited. Then a special anticodon signals the end of the protein synthesis process. The resulting chain of amino acids is called a protein.

RNA is also the carrier of genetic information in certain viruses, while DNA performs this function in other viruses. There is some evidence that cancer-causing viruses are usually RNA viruses.
See also CANCER; DNA; GENE.

ROADRUNNER A roadrunner is a bird that belongs to the cuckoo family, Cuculidae. It is found in the dry areas of Mexico and the southwestern United States. The bird runs rapidly along the ground and got its name because it used to run after horses and coaches to snap up the insects, lizards, and snakes that were disturbed. It even kills rattlesnakes. The roadrunner is a large bird, growing to a length of 22 in. [55 cm]. It has brown and white feathers and a patch of blue and red skin behind its eyes. The roadrunner rarely flies, but can run at about 12 m.p.h. [20 kph].

ROADRUNNER
The roadrunner is found in the dry areas of Mexico and the southwestern United States.

ROBIN A robin is a kind of thrush (see THRUSH). It is a very common bird in North America. A robin is easily recognized by its brownish black back and orange chest and belly. It grows to a length of 8.5 in. [21.3 cm]. Robins are often seen on grassy lawns hunting for insects and worms to eat. They also feed on berries and seeds.

Many robins fly south for the winter and return to northern lands for the summer. An old tradition states that the sight of a robin is the first sign of spring. That may not always be accurate, however, because many robins spend the winter in northern lands.

The European robin is smaller and browner than the American robin, and has pale feathers at the base of the tail.

ROBIN—American species
The robin is a common North American bird. Most robins fly to warmer southern climates in winter and return north for the summer.

ROBIN—European species
The European robin is smaller than the American robin with pale—almost white—feathers at the base of the tail.

ROBOTICS (rō bŏt′ĭks) Robotics is the science that deals with the design and the use of robots. A robot is a machine that is often used to perform a variety of tasks in place of humans. A robot is controlled by computer programs (sets of instructions) (see COMPUTER).

Robots are used throughout industry. Manufacturers use industrial robots for tasks that are repetitive and often boring, such as welding automobile bodies, performing certain laboratory tests, and assembling electronic components. Robots are frequently used to handle dangerous or heavy materials. Robots are also used to perform tasks in places that are unhealthy for humans, such as places with poisonous fumes or wastes or those with a high level of noise.

The armlike devices of the earliest industrial robots could only perform simple tasks, such as moving heavy materials from one place to another. This was largely because the computer programs that operated the robots were very limited and difficult to change. Advances in computer programming have allowed today's industrial robots to perform complex tasks and to be reprogrammed to change their tasks. Today's robots also have intricate "hands," "fingers," and other parts that allow them to perform delicate tasks accurately. For example, robots can assemble watches and computers.

Robotics is not a new science. Its roots date back to about A.D. 1000, when machines were built that imitated a limited range of human actions. These machines are called automatons or androids (see ANDROID). Clock makers often built automatons to ring bells or wave flags when the clock struck. Automatons are used today in industry for some simple tasks. An automaton is not a true robot, however. According to the Robot Institute of America, a true robot must be able to be reprogrammed to perform a variety of tasks.

Modern robotics The story of modern robotics probably began with the invention of servomechanisms in the 1940s. A servomechanism is a system that detects and corrects errors made by a machine. The servomechanism detects the errors by a sensing device. The device signals a servomotor in the machine. The servomotor then corrects the error. Many machines used in heavy industry, such as lathes, are equipped with servomechanisms (see LATHE). The servomechanism detects when the lathe starts cutting a material, such as wood, in a way that is different from the intended shape. The error is then corrected. The automatic pilots in airplanes are also servomechanisms. An automatic pilot is a device that flies the plane without the actual pilot having to use the controls. The automatic pilot can detect when the airplane starts to travel off course and then correct the airplane's direction.

The invention and development of the computer from the late 1930s through the 1950s set the stage for the great leap forward made by robotics in the 1960s. By the end of the 1970s and 1980s, computerized robots had replaced many human workers, especially in automobile factories.

Generally, an industrial robot has a base that may house its computer "brain." The base is equipped with parts that act like a shoulder, arm, wrist, hand, and fingers. Robots can sometimes more closely resemble humans in that they may have two shoulders, arms, and so on. The arm and shoulder can swing around in all directions, and the wrist can bend to move the hand. The hand can open and close its fingers to grasp or release objects. Using these movements, the robot can do tasks quickly and in exactly the same way thousands of times without stopping. It makes fewer mistakes than a human worker does. It can also be programmed to check its work and correct any mistakes it does make. Because today's robots can be easily reprogrammed, manufacturers can adapt their production lines quickly to new products or changes in existing products. In addition, robot labor often costs less than human labor.

In the last few years, robotics has made significant advancements. One of these advancements is to give robots "senses" that are similar to human senses (see SENSE). For example, today's robots have electronic "sight." In the past, if a robot's task was

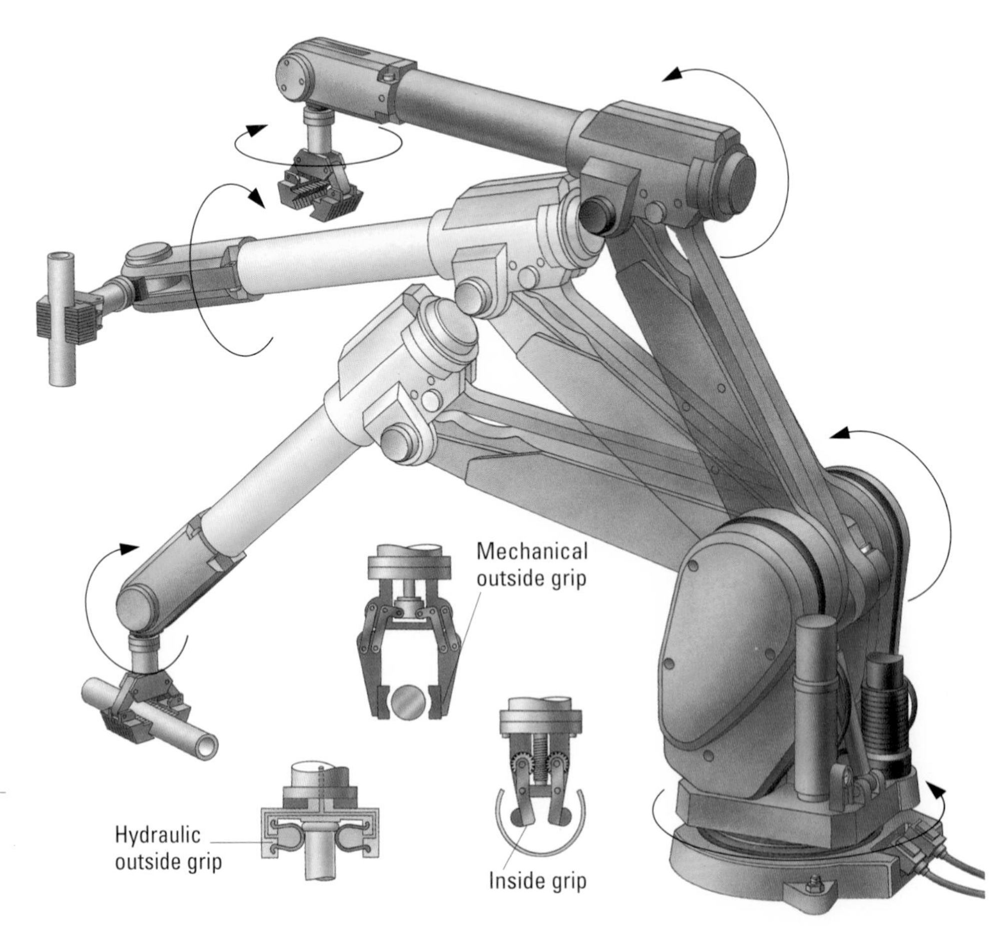

ROBOTICS—Mechanical arms

Modern robots have a wide range of movements and can be fitted with various kinds of "hands" to grip objects of different shapes.

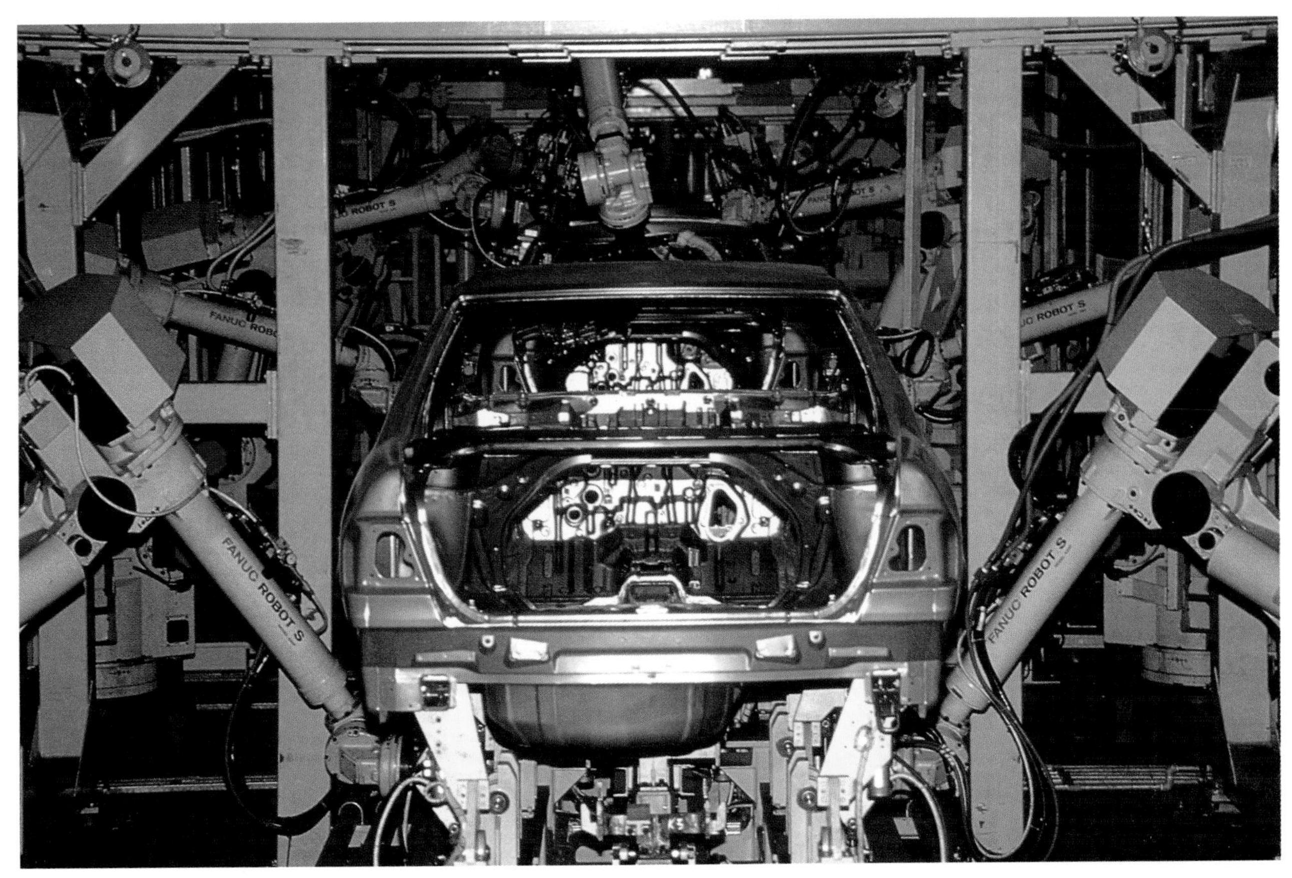

ROBOTICS—Making automobiles

Automobile manufacturing has benefited greatly from the use of robots. The robots are programmed to carry out the same tasks over and over again quickly and accurately.

to assemble parts, all of the parts had to be presented to it in a certain position. However, a robot today performing the same task can reach into a pile of jumbled parts, "see" the part it needs, and pick it up.

Artificial intelligence is another advancement in robotics (see ARTIFICIAL INTELLIGENCE). In artificial intelligence, a computer can be programmed to "think" and "reason" like a human. This means that a robot with such a computer can "remember" its past mistakes and not make them again. It gets better at solving problems by learning from experience.

The future of robotics It is difficult to predict the future of robotics because changes in computer technology are occurring so quickly. However, it is safe to say that tomorrow's robots will be faster and "smarter" than today's robots. In addition, their arms and hands will be designed in such a way that they will be able to handle even more delicate tasks. Some scientists believe that this will mean that humans will be able to enjoy improved products at lower prices.

ROCK Rock is the solid material that makes up the earth's crust. Most rock is a mixture of various minerals. It lacks a definite chemical composition because of the different types and amounts of minerals present in the rock (see EARTH; MINERAL).

Eight elements make up 98 percent of all rock on Earth. These elements are: oxygen, silicon, aluminum, iron, calcium, sodium, potassium, and magnesium (see ELEMENT). A large portion of the rocks on Earth are silicates. Silicates are a combination of silicon and oxygen, together with various other elements.

Because rocks lack a definite chemical composition, they are not classified by the elements they contain. Instead, geologists (scientists who study the earth) classify rocks according to the way they formed (see GEOLOGY). There are three main types of rock: igneous rock, metamorphic rock, and sedimentary rock.

ROCK

The rugged inland cliffs (below) are made of chalk, a type of organic (carbon-containing) sedimentary rock.

Igneous rock Igneous rock forms from the cooling and crystallization of a material called magma. Magma is melted rock that has been subjected to high temperature and great pressure beneath the earth's surface. There are two types of igneous rock: extrusive and intrusive.

Extrusive igneous rock forms when magma breaks through the crust and cools on the surface of the earth, as in a volcanic eruption. The magma is called lava when it reaches the surface. Its quick cooling does not allow time for large crystals to form. Types of extrusive rocks include pumice, basalt, and obsidian. Extrusive igneous rocks account for only about 5 percent of all igneous rock types (see CRYSTAL; LAVA; MAGMA; VOLCANO).

Intrusive igneous rock forms when magma cools below the surface. Since the magma cools relatively slowly, there is time for large crystals to form. Granite is a type of intrusive igneous rock (see IGNEOUS ROCK).

Metamorphic rock Metamorphic rock is rock that has changed in appearance or composition.

ACTIVITY *See how rocks form*

Take several flat toothpicks, some short lengths of drinking straw, and some small pieces of paper. Fold the toothpicks and straws in half, and crumple the paper into small balls. Pile them together on a table and press down on them with a large book. When you remove the book, the materials will be flattened into layers. In much the same way, the pressure of overlying rocks flattens rocks beneath to form layers of metamorphic rock.

The changes are caused by heat, pressure, or chemical changes beneath the earth's surface. A metamorphic rock has changed its mineral composition while still in the solid state. If it had melted, it would have become an igneous rock.

Types of metamorphic rocks include marble, quartzite, and slate (see METAMORPHIC ROCK).

Sedimentary rock Sedimentary rock is formed from the accumulation of sediment under water or on land. The sediment deposits consist of loose sand and pebbles and the remains of dead animals and plants. Eventually, pressure from above causes the accumulation of material to harden into rock. There are several types of sedimentary rock. Clastic sedimentary rocks consist of rock fragments of various sizes, compacted and cemented together. Clastic rocks include sandstone and shale. Some sedimentary rocks are made of minerals that were once dissolved in water. Crystallization occurred when the water evaporated. Examples of this type of sedimentary rock include flint and gypsum. Organic sedimentary rocks are formed from the remains of dead plants and animals. Organic sedimentary rocks include coal and chalk (see SEDIMENTARY ROCK).

Sedimentary rocks are geologically important because they form in layers called strata. Each stratum (singular of *strata*) yields valuable information about the conditions of the time period it represents. The strata are often rich in fossils.

See also FOSSIL; ROCK CYCLE. PROJECT 20

ROCK CYCLE Rocks are constantly being created and destroyed. This continuing process is called the rock cycle. The three types of rock are igneous, sedimentary, and metamorphic (see IGNEOUS ROCK; SEDIMENTARY ROCK; METAMORPHIC ROCK). No matter which type is eroded (worn away), the fragments produce sedimentary rock when they are deposited.

Igneous rock is formed as molten (melted) material solidifies beneath or on the surface of the earth. As the earth's surface is worn away, deeper bodies of rock are exposed at the surface, including igneous rock that solidified beneath the surface. This is also worn away by the weathering, and the crumbled fragments are washed away by rivers and streams. These fragments may accumulate on the seabed as a layer of sediment and become buried by other layers. Eventually these layers will be compacted and cemented together and become sedimentary rock. At a later time these sedimentary rocks, along with the other two rock types, may be crumpled up into a mountain range. The heat and pressure may be so great that they are changed into metamorphic rocks. Eventually these metamorphic rocks, too, become exposed at the surface and wear away, with the fragments deposited as sediments.

Other routes through the cycle may involve the sedimentary rocks melting at great depth and becoming igneous rocks, igneous rocks being compressed into metamorphic rocks, or even sedimentary rocks wearing away and accumulating as more sedimentary rocks.

See also GEOLOGY; ROCK; WEATHERING.

ROCKET

A rocket is a type of engine in which force is produced as a reaction to the exhaust of burned fuels. *Rocket* also refers to the type of cylinder-shaped craft that generally is propelled by a rocket engine (see FORCE).

A basic law of motion discovered in the 1600s by Sir Isaac Newton describes how rockets work. This law states that for any action, there is an equal and opposite reaction (see DYNAMICS; MOTION, LAWS OF). For example, if air is released from a balloon, it drives the balloon forward in flight. A rocket works in much the same way.

A rocket engine produces more force for its size than any other type of engine (see ENGINE). For example, a rocket engine the size of an automobile engine produces three thousand times more force than the automobile engine. Another kind of engine that works in much the same way as a rocket

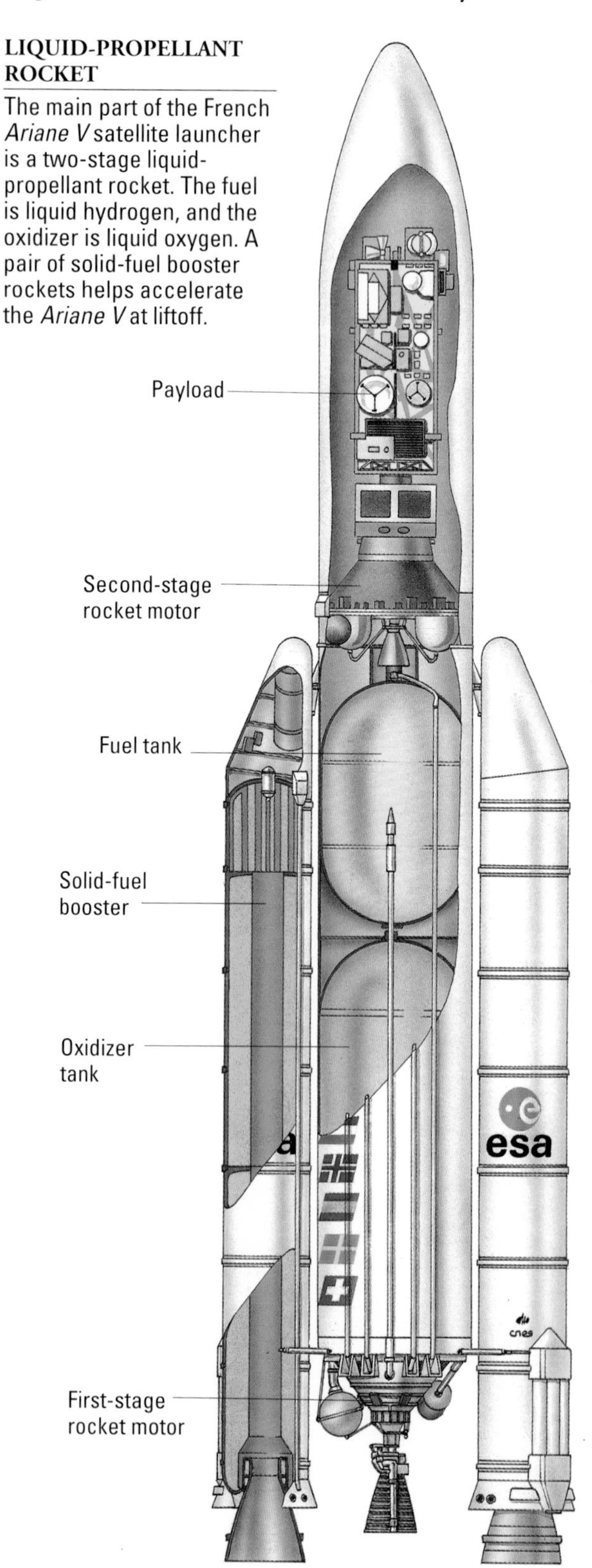

LIQUID-PROPELLANT ROCKET

The main part of the French *Ariane V* satellite launcher is a two-stage liquid-propellant rocket. The fuel is liquid hydrogen, and the oxidizer is liquid oxygen. A pair of solid-fuel booster rockets helps accelerate the *Ariane V* at liftoff.

Fuel
Oxidizer
Combustion chamber
Exhaust

ROCKET PRINCIPLE

In a rocket, combustion (burning) of a fuel in the combustion chamber (sometimes with the aid of an oxidizer) produces hot gases at high pressure. The pressure pushes in all directions. The action of the gases forming the exhaust causes a reaction that propels the rocket forward.

engine is a jet engine. The difference between a rocket engine and a jet engine is that a rocket engine carries a supply of oxygen, called an oxidizer, to burn the fuel. The oxidizer and fuel together are called the propellant (see COMBUSTION). The jet engine, on the other hand, sucks oxygen in from the atmosphere. This is why jets cannot fly above the earth's atmosphere, while rockets can.

People use rockets of many sizes and types. Some rockets are used to shoot fireworks into the sky. These rockets are only about 2 ft. [0.6 m] long. Rockets that are 50 to 100 ft. [15 to 30 m] long are used to carry missiles (see MISSILE). The largest rocket—*Saturn V*, which carried the first astronauts to the moon—stood more than 360 ft. [110 m] high (see SPACE EXPLORATION).

Rockets have been used in war for hundreds of years. The weapons carried by today's military rockets can destroy airplanes and missiles flying faster than the speed of sound. Scientists use rockets for exploration and research in the atmosphere and space. For example, rockets have launched hundreds of satellites into orbit around the earth (see SATELLITE). These satellites take pictures of the earth's weather, gather other information for scientific study, and serve commercial uses as well. Many satellites are used to transmit radio, telephone, and television signals around the world.

Rockets that are used for long flights through the atmosphere and for space exploration are called multistage rockets. Multistage rockets consist of two or more sections called stages. Each stage has its own propellant supply. A multistage rocket can reach higher speeds and travel farther than a single-stage rocket because it lightens its weight by dropping one or more stages as it uses up propellant. Most space rockets have two or three stages. The first stage in a multistage space rocket is called the booster. It launches the rocket off its launching pad. For the booster stage, a propellant that can provide a high thrust is needed to overcome the earth's gravity. The main purpose of the upper stages is to build velocity (see VELOCITY).

Space rockets are launched in a step-by-step process called a countdown. A specific action is required at each step. When the countdown reaches zero, the rocket lifts off the launching pad and begins its journey. Sometimes, bad weather or some mechanical difficulty may cause a "hold," which temporarily stops the countdown. A countdown for a large space rocket can last several days.

***SATURN* ROCKET**

The *Saturn* series of rockets were developed by NASA. They had to be powerful enough to launch three astronauts to the moon. Here the *Saturn V* rocket lifts off on the Apollo 16 moon mission.

Rocket propellant When the rocket propellant is burned, the temperature in some rocket engines reaches 6,000°F [3,300°C]. Hot gas is created at a high pressure inside the rocket. The pressure of the gas on one side of the rocket balances the pressure on the opposite side of the rocket. However, the gas flowing to the rear of the rocket escapes through a nozzle. This exhaust gas does not balance the gas pressure against the front of the rocket. It is this uneven pressure that drives the rocket forward. The force with which the rocket is driven forward is called thrust. The production of motion in one direction because of the release of gas in the opposite direction is called jet propulsion (see JET PROPULSION; THRUST).

Rocket propellants burn rapidly, and most rockets or rocket stages carry a supply that lasts only a few minutes. However, this burning produces such great power that it can hurl vehicles weighing many tons far into space. The rocket's speed is held down in the first few minutes of flight by air friction, gravity, and the weight of the unburned propellant and the stages (see FRICTION; GRAVITY). As the rocket climbs higher, the air becomes thinner, so air friction decreases. There is no air friction at all in space. Also, the pull of the earth's gravity decreases as the rocket travels farther from Earth. In addition, the rocket becomes lighter as it burns up propellant and drops its stages.

Kinds of propulsion systems There are four basic kinds of rocket propulsion systems: solid propellant; liquid propellant; electric; and nuclear.

Solid-propellant rockets burn a plasticlike material called grain. The grain consists of a solid fuel and a solid oxidizer. Grain may be ignited (caused to burn) in several ways. It may be ignited by first burning a small amount of a certain powder in a part of the engine called the igniter. Grain may also be ignited by the chemical reaction that occurs between a liquid chlorine compound and grain when the chlorine is sprayed onto the grain (see CHEMICAL REACTION; COMPOUND). Solid propellants burn faster than liquid propellants, but they produce less thrust per unit weight. However, the solid propellant is easy to handle, remains effective during long periods of storage, and does not explode easily. Solid propellants are used mainly by the military.

Liquid-propellant rockets burn a mixture of a liquid fuel and a liquid oxidizer. Cryogenic methods are used to turn certain fuels into liquids (see CRYOGENICS). Some liquid propellants, called hypergols, ignite because of the chemical reaction that occurs when the fuel and oxidizer contact each other. However, most liquid propellants require a complicated ignition system. The creation of an electric spark or the burning of a small amount of solid propellant can be used for ignition. Liquid propellants burn more slowly than solid propellants, but they produce more thrust per unit weight. Liquid propellants are more difficult to handle and store. Scientists use liquid-propellant rockets for space launch vehicles.

Electric rockets use electric power either to heat a gas or to produce electrically charged particles called ions. The hot gas or the ions produce thrust (see IONS AND IONIZATION). Electric rockets can operate longer than solid- and liquid-propellant rockets, but they produce much less thrust. For example, an electric rocket could not lift a heavy spacecraft out of the earth's atmosphere. However, once outside the pull of the earth's gravity, an electric rocket could propel a spacecraft through space reaching very high speeds.

Nuclear rockets heat liquid fuel by means of a nuclear reactor (see NUCLEAR ENERGY). The fuel turns into hot, rapidly expanding gas that flows from the rocket. Scientists are working on the development of electric and nuclear rockets for future space travel.

History Rockets were first used by Chinese armies around A.D. 1232. The armies propelled the rockets toward enemy troops. By 1300, the use of rockets for war had spread throughout Europe and Asia. These early rockets burned a compound of charcoal, saltpeter (a form of potassium nitrate), and sulfur as fuel. During the early 1800s, Colonel William Congreve of the British army developed rockets that could carry explosives. Rockets have been used in every major war since.

In 1926, Robert H. Goddard, an American scientist, conducted the first successful launching of a liquid-propellant rocket. Goddard became a world leader in rocket development and research and is known today as "The Father of Modern Rocketry" (see GODDARD, ROBERT HUTCHINGS).

During World War II (1939–1945), huge guided rockets, called *V-2s*, were developed by German scientists for use in war. A guided rocket is one that can be directed by a computer or other equipment after it is launched. These first guided rockets were the forerunners of today's space rockets. Many of the German scientists, including Wernher von Braun, came to the United States after the war to help develop military and space rockets (see BRAUN, WERNHER VON).

A series of rocket-powered airplanes, the *X-1* through the *X-15,* set world airplane speed and altitude records through the 1950s and 1960s. The *X-15* established a new altitude record of 67 mi. [108 km] in 1963 and then set a speed record of 4,520 m.p.h. [7,274 kph] in 1967.

The "space age" began on October 4, 1957,

ROCKET HISTORY

The American engineer Robert H. Goddard (far left) is known as "The Father of Modern Rocketry." He built the first successful liquid-propellant rocket in 1926.

when the Soviet Union launched the first artificial satellite, *Sputnik I,* into orbit around the earth using a multistage rocket. On April 12, 1961, a rocket launched a Soviet spacecraft carrying the first person, cosmonaut (astronaut) Yuri Gagarin, into space (see GAGARIN, YURI ALEKSEYEVICH; SPUTNIK).

Today, space rockets are being used more and more to launch satellites into orbit. Before 1981, space rockets were not reusable. Most space rockets were burned away during or after the launch. Because it cost so much to build these rockets that burned up after only one use, scientists began to research building a reusable space rocket. The first spacecraft to be equipped with a reusable space rocket was the space shuttle *Columbia. Columbia* was first launched from Cape Canaveral, Florida, on April 12, 1981 (see CAPE CANAVERAL).

The shuttle consists of several parts. The external fuel tank, which consists of tanks of liquefied oxygen and hydrogen, is joined by a load-bearing intertank, which carries the propellants for the main engines. Two solid-propellant boosters are attached to the sides of the liquid-fuel tank. The orbiter, which has three main rocket engines, is attached to the front of the fuel tank. The boosters help launch the shuttle. They fall to the earth by parachute two minutes after the shuttle lifts off from the launching pad. The boosters are recovered and reused. The large fuel tank drops off eight minutes after liftoff and breaks up over the ocean. The orbiter's three rocket engines provide the final power to enter orbit. Later, the orbiter uses these three engines to reenter the earth's atmosphere and land on a runway. The space shuttle is designed to be reused up to a hundred times.

Rockets of the future Rockets of the future may carry people to the nearest stars and beyond. They may be used to take thousands of people off the crowded Earth to colonize some distant planet. Nuclear rockets may be the key to reaching these great distances, or some new form of power for rockets may emerge. Rockets also may become a means of rapid travel on Earth. It might be possible to travel from New York to England in fifteen minutes. The future for rockets seems almost limitless.

See also ACCELERATION.

ROCK SALT Rock salt is a mineral that occurs in rocklike deposits. It is a compound of sodium and chlorine, called sodium chloride (NaCl). Rock salt is also called halite or table salt (see COMPOUND; MINERAL; SODIUM CHLORIDE).

Pure rock salt is colorless and occurs as transparent or semitransparent crystals (see CRYSTAL). Purple or blue discolorations in rock salt beds are due to unbonded sodium (sodium that has not combined with chlorine) in the deposit.

Beds of rock salt are found on all the continents and beneath the oceans. In deserts and other dry regions, the deposits may be close to the surface. In many other areas, the rock salt is covered by layers of sedimentary rock (see SEDIMENTARY ROCK).

Natural rock salt is the direct result of evaporation. Salty lakes and marshes dried up during periods of drought (little or no rain). They left behind large amounts of salt. This rock salt occurs in sedimentary rock, often associated with limestone, gypsum, or shale.

Rock salt is used on roadways during the winter to melt snow and ice. It has hundreds of other industrial uses as well.

See also SALTS.

ROCK SALT

Rock salt, or halite, usually occurs as cubic crystals. It has many uses in the chemical industry.

RODENT (rōd'nt) Rodents form a large order of mammals, including the rat, mouse, squirrel, beaver, and porcupine (see MAMMAL). There are about two thousand kinds of rodents—nearly as many as all the other kinds of mammals put together. Rodents are characterized by the two pairs of sharp chisellike teeth at the front of the mouth. The front part of each tooth is usually orange and is much harder than the rest of the tooth. As the teeth work against each other, the hind part is worn away more rapidly than the front, and the chisel-shaped edge is maintained. The teeth grow continuously from the roots to make up for the wear at the tip.

Rodents gnaw most of the time. The name *rodent* comes from the Latin word *rodere,* meaning "to gnaw." Besides their use for gnawing food, the teeth are used for digging burrows or for shredding twigs.

Most of the rodents are herbivores, feeding

RODENT

Common rodents include rats, mice, and squirrels, all of which are found throughout the world. Shown here are (1) the South American climbing rat, (2) the African pygmy squirrel, and (3) the Siberian chipmunk.

mainly on seeds and grasses. Some are omnivorous and eat almost anything (see HERBIVORE; OMNIVORE). Rats and mice are in this category.

Mice are the smallest rodents. The largest rodent is the capybara, which lives in South America. Some capybaras grow to 4 ft. [1.2 m] in length.

Population explosions occur from time to time among the mice and voles and particularly among the lemmings (see LEMMING). However, high densities are unusual. The rodent population is normally kept from growing too fast by a variety of carnivores (meat-eating animals), such as cats, foxes, weasels, hawks, and owls.

To humans, rodents can be both harmful and helpful. Rats, mice, voles, and other species often do a great deal of damage to human food supplies and crops. Rats also do considerable damage to buildings, and rats and mice can carry serious diseases. Some rodents—for example, beavers, chinchillas, and muskrats—are valued for their fur. Rats, mice, and guinea pigs are frequently used in laboratory research. Guinea pigs are also kept as pets, as are hamsters, gerbils, and several other kinds of rodents.

ROEMER, OLAUS (1644–1710) (rā′ mər, ō′ lous) Olaus Roemer was a Danish astronomer. He worked with the French astronomer Jean Picard. While he was in Paris, France, Roemer studied the satellites (moons) of the planet Jupiter. Another astronomer had already discovered how long these satellites took to orbit (travel around) Jupiter. Roemer watched as they eclipsed (disappeared from view) behind Jupiter. He found that the eclipses occurred earlier when the earth was nearer to Jupiter than when it was farther away.

Roemer set to work to find out why this happened. He had an idea that it might be because the light took longer to get to the earth when Jupiter was farther away. This was a new idea. It meant that light must travel at a certain speed. Until then, astronomers thought that light did not take any time at all to get from one place to another. Roemer did many experiments to find out how fast light actually traveled. He calculated that it was 141,000 mi. [227,000 km] per second. We now know that the speed of light is 186,282 mi. [299,792 km] per second. Other scientists at that time could not agree about Roemer's idea. It was not accepted until 1728, when other scientists confirmed Roemer's theory.

See also ECLIPSE; LIGHT.

ROENTGEN (rĕnt′gən) A roentgen, named for the discoverer of X rays, Wilhelm Roentgen, is a unit used to measure exposure from X rays and gamma rays. When these radiations pass through air, they cause ionization (see IONS AND IONIZATION). A roentgen (symbol R) is defined as the amount of radiation that is sufficient to cause the production of one electrostatic unit of charge in 0.00005 oz. [0.001293 g] of air. Roentgens are used in medical radiology. The unit may also be spelled *röntgen.* In many places, the roentgen has been replaced by the SI (International System of Units, or metric system) unit, coulomb per kilogram. There is 0.000258 coulomb per kilogram in 1 roentgen.

See also ELECTROSTATICS; GAMMA RAY; RADIATION; RADIOLOGY; ROENTGEN, WILHELM CONRAD; X RAY.

ROENTGEN, WILHELM CONRAD (1845–1923) (rĕnt′ gən, wĭl′ hĕlm kŏn′ răd) Wilhelm Roentgen (also spelled Röntgen) was a German physicist. In 1895, Roentgen was using a vacuum tube to study the effect of electricity on gases. He noticed that a fluorescent screen that had been placed a short distance from the tube glowed when the tube was in use (see FLUORESCENCE; VACUUM TUBE). Roentgen found that the fluorescent screen glowed even when the tube was wrapped in heavy black paper. Roentgen believed that invisible rays were causing this effect. He called the rays X rays because he did not know what they were. They are still called X rays and are very important in many fields of science.

Roentgen realized the importance of this discovery. He went on to do many careful experiments on this form of radiation. The first Nobel Prize for physics went to Roentgen in 1901.

See also ELECTRONICS; RADIATION; ROENTGEN; X RAY.

ROOT In most plants, roots are the structures that anchor the plant and absorb water and dissolved minerals. The roots of most plants grow underground. All types of roots have the same basic structure. The tip is covered by the root cap, which is made of dead cells. The root cap protects the tip as the root grows downward through the soil. Many root cap cells are rubbed off in this process. They are constantly being replaced by apical meristem cells located just inside the root cap, in the root tip (see MERISTEM). Meristem cells are any plant cells that divide rapidly, producing many more cells (see MITOSIS). In the zone of elongation, above the apical meristem, the meristem cells become longer, causing the root to increase in length and pushing the tip further down into the ground. After the cells elongate, they begin to specialize, so they can perform various functions. This occurs in the zone of maturation (see DIFFERENTIATION, CELLULAR).

In a cross section of a root, the outermost cells make up the epidermis. Some of these epidermal cells produce tiny outgrowths called root hairs. These root hairs greatly increase the surface available for absorbing water and minerals. Inside the epidermis is a layer of spongy tissue called the cortex. It stores food (see CORTEX). Inside the cortex is a central cylinder. The central cylinder contains cambium, xylem, and phloem. In the very center of this cylinder in some roots is the pith, which also stores food. The cambium produces new xylem and phloem, which results in an increase in the root's diameter (see CAMBIUM). The xylem is made of tough, tubular cells that transport water and minerals from the root upward to the leaves (see XYLEM). The phloem is made of cells that transport food downward from the leaves, where it is made (see PHLOEM).

Most of the water and dissolved minerals taken in by a root are absorbed by the tiny root hairs. The water and minerals then move toward the central cylinder. They move from one cell to the next by osmosis and diffusion (see DIFFUSION; OSMOSIS). Once they reach the xylem, the water and minerals begin their trip up through the root, into the stem, to the leaves. Water and minerals are needed by the leaves for photosynthesis (see PHOTOSYNTHESIS). As a root grows, it needs oxygen. It gets this oxygen from tiny air spaces in the soil. If these air spaces become filled with water, such as after a heavy rainstorm, the roots may not have any source of oxygen, and they may die.

Basically, there are two types of root systems:

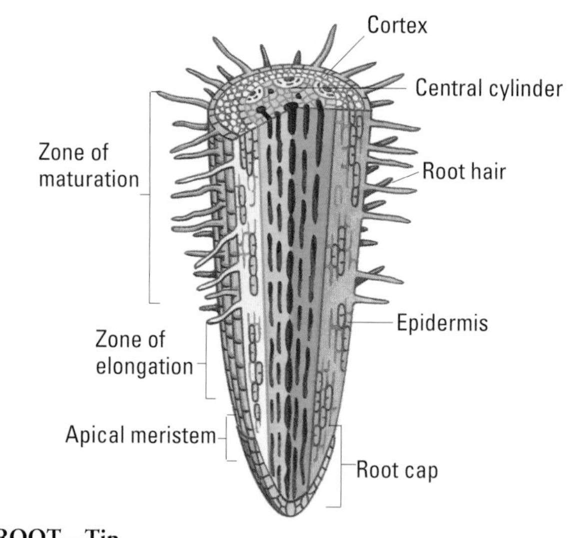

ROOT—Tip
The various parts of the growing tip of a root are shown above.

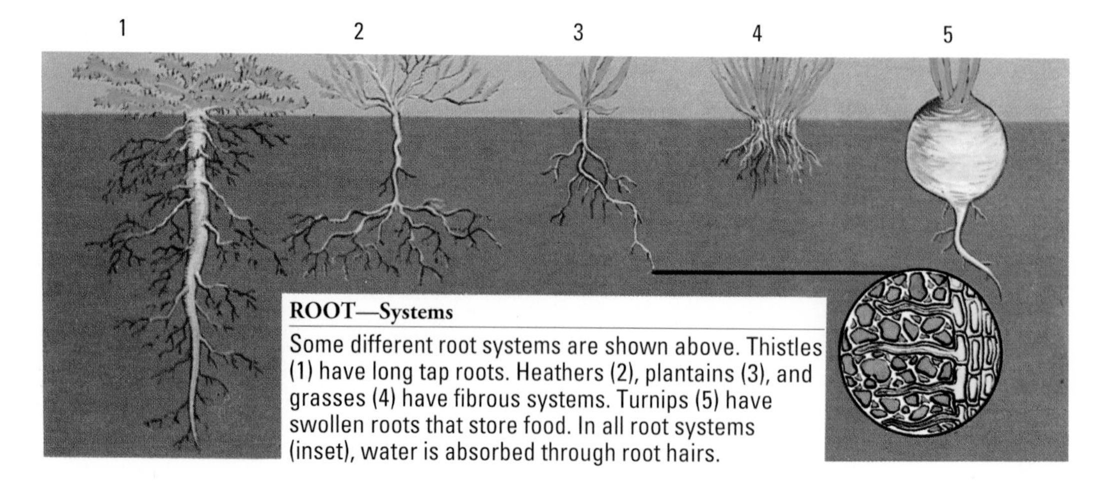

ROOT—Systems
Some different root systems are shown above. Thistles (1) have long tap roots. Heathers (2), plantains (3), and grasses (4) have fibrous systems. Turnips (5) have swollen roots that store food. In all root systems (inset), water is absorbed through root hairs.

fibrous and tap. In fibrous root systems, there are many main roots, all of which are about the same size. In tap root systems, there is one large main root. Some tap roots, such as carrots and turnips, are swollen with stored food supplies (see ROOT CROP). Some fibrous roots also swell up with food and are then called root tubers. Dahlias have tubers of this kind. Smaller roots grow from the main roots in both fibrous and tap systems. Although most roots grow in the ground, some do not. Aerial roots grow in the air (see EPIPHYTE).

Some plants produce roots from stems or leaves. These roots are called adventitious roots. They often provide extra support for a plant. In corn, for example, adventitious roots grow into the ground from buds located partway up the stem. Adventitious roots like these are sometimes called prop roots. Ivy also produces adventitious roots, which help its stems to cling to walls and other supports (see IVY). The roots produced by rhizomes are also said to be adventitious (see RHIZOME). Some plants are parasites. They produce special roots that absorb water, food, and other substances from the cells of a host (see PARASITE). Some plant roots live symbiotically with a fungus (see SYMBIOSIS). In this situation, the fungus provides water and minerals to the root in exchange for shelter and food from the plant.
See also PLANT KINGDOM; VASCULAR PLANT.

ROOT CROP The roots of some plants are swollen with stored food. These roots can be eaten as vegetables. The plants that produce such roots are called root crops. The most popular root crops are beets, carrots, radishes, rutabagas, sweet potatoes, and turnips.
See also ROOT.

ROOT, MATHEMATICAL When a number is multiplied by itself, the result is called the square of that number. For example, 2 x 2 = 4, and 5 x 5 = 25. The numbers 4 and 25 are the squares of 2 and 5. Put the other way around, 2 is the square root of 4, and 5 is the square root of 25. A positive number can have a negative square root. For example, -5 is a square root of 25 because -5 x -5 = 25. When a number is multiplied by itself once and then again, the result is called the cube of the number. For example, 3 x 3 x 3 = 27. The cube of 3 is 27, and the cube root of 27 is 3. There are several ways of writing the root of a number. The usual way is to use the sign called a root bar, or vinculum, $\sqrt{}$. The square root of 25 is written $\sqrt{25}$. The cube root of 27 is written $\sqrt[3]{27}$. Another way of writing a square root is $(25)^{1/2}$.
See also NUMBER.

RORQUAL (rôr′kwəl) *Rorqual* is a term used to describe baleen whales that have grooves on their throats and undersides and small fins on their backs. Rorquals include the blue, fin, humpback, minke, and sei whales (see WHALE).

A rorqual has from ten to one hundred grooves that are 1 to 2 in. [2.5 to 5.1 cm] deep. The grooves extend from the chin to the navel and cover about half of the whale's underside.

ROSE FAMILY The rose family includes nearly three thousand species of herbaceous plants, shrubs, and trees. These dicotyledonous plants grow throughout the world (see DICOTYLEDON; HERBACEOUS PLANT). They have a wide range of leaf shapes, from the simple leaves of the apple to the three-lobed leaves of the strawberry and the pinnately (arranged like a feather) compound leaves of the rose (see LEAF). The flowers grow singly or in clusters at the ends of stems. They usually have five petals and five sepals. They have many stamens and one or more pistils (see FLOWER).

The fruits produced by members of the rose family are highly varied. Some plants, such as the spiraea, have dry fruits. Some, such as the apricot, cherry, peach, plum, and nectarine, produce drupes, or stone fruit (see DRUPE). The raspberry produces fruits that are actually clusters of drupelets. In some plants, such as the strawberry, the seeds grow on the outside of a fleshy receptacle (see RECEPTACLE). In apple, hawthorn, mountain ash, and pear fruits, the fleshy receptacle encloses the seeds (see POME).

The many species of roses all belong to genus *Rosa.* Most of these grow in temperate areas. Some roses are climbing or creeping plants. Others are small shrubs. Most have prickly stems. Roses are often grown for their beautiful flowers. The flowers may be almost any color except blue. Many cultivated varieties have a double set of petals. One of the most popular species of rose is the tea rose. The tea rose is often crossed with other species to produce hybrids (see HYBRID).

Rose petals produce an oil that can be used in perfume and other cosmetic products. The fruit is called a hip. Rose hips are rich in vitamin C and are often made into jellies and jams.

ROSE FAMILY

Modern cultivated roses, such as the double-petaled hybrid tea rose (top), were developed from various kinds of wild rose (bottom).

ROSEWOOD Rosewood is the common name for several species of tropical trees belonging to genus *Dalbergia* of the pea family. The trees have a dark, reddish brown wood that, when cut with a saw, smells like roses. This wood is very hard and is often used in furniture and musical instruments. Some of these trees are becoming very rare because so many have been cut down for timber.
See also PEA FAMILY.

ROTIFER (rō′tə fər) A rotifer is a tiny animal that commonly lives in still, fresh water. It belongs to the class Rotifera. Its shape usually resembles that of a tiny worm. The name *rotifer* comes from the Latin words for "wheel bearer" and refers to the circle of projections called cilia on the animal's head (see CILIUM). The rotifer uses these cilia to swim and to sweep food into its mouth. The animal's foot gives off a sticky substance that holds it in place while it feeds. The rotifer's food consists chiefly of other microscopic plants and animals.

Some rotifers live on land. These terrestrial (land-dwelling) rotifers can live up to four years in an inactive state while they are dry, and then burst into life again when wetted. They can also survive extreme cold.

RUBBER *Rubber* can refer to any of a number of materials that share certain properties. These properties include elasticity (ability to stretch and spring back into shape), flexibility (ability to bend), resistance to electric current, low permeability (ability to be penetrated) by gases and liquids, and resistance to abrasion (scratches and chips). Natural rubber comes from liquids secreted (given out) by certain plants. Synthetic rubber is made from chemicals.

Natural rubber Natural rubber is made from latex, a milky liquid secreted by several kinds of plants, including dandelion and goldenrod. Almost all natural rubber comes from rubber trees that originally grew in the rain forests of South America (see RUBBER TREE). Later, these trees also were grown on huge plantations (farms) in the East Indies, southeast Asia, and parts of Africa.

To get latex from a rubber tree, several diagonal cuts are made in the bark 2 to 5 ft. [0.6 to 1.5 m] above the ground. The bark between cuts is removed so that latex can run down to the end of the lowest cut and drip into a container. This process is called tapping the tree.

Latex contains a polymer of a hydrocarbon called isoprene (see HYDROCARBON; POLYMER). Isoprene has the chemical formula C_5H_8. It has four carbon atoms in a row, each end pair being joined by two bonds. The fifth carbon atom is linked to one of these pairs. This same pair is also linked to two hydrogen atoms. Three hydrogen atoms are linked to the single carbon atom, and three more hydrogen atoms are linked to the other carbon pair. Isoprene molecules can join end to end. In natural rubber, each polymer molecule has thousands of isoprene units joined in this way. The polymer molecules have a natural tendency to coil up. They can be straightened by pulling, but return to their coiled position when released. This is why rubber is elastic.

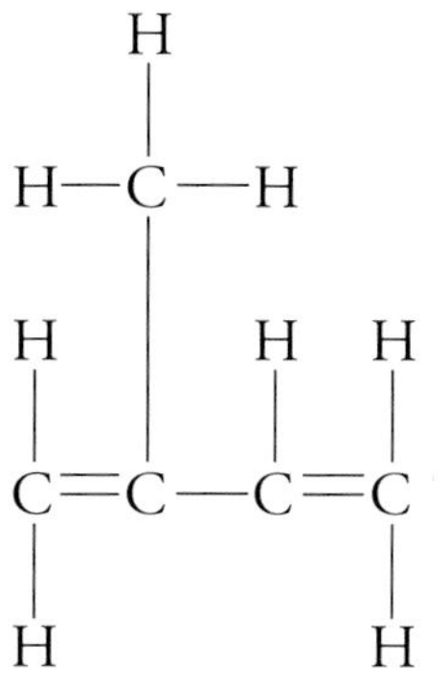

```
     H
     |
  H—C—H
     |
H    |    H  H
|    |    |  |
C═C—C═C
|          |
H          H
```

RUBBER—Isoprene
Natural rubber is a polymer of the hydrocarbon chemical isoprene, whose structural formula is shown (left).

By weight, latex consists of about 30 to 35 percent rubber and 60 to 65 percent water. The rest of latex consists of small amounts of such materials as sugars, proteins, and salts. After being tapped from the tree, latex is put into tanks with water. The now diluted latex is strained for impurities, such as dirt and bits of bark. Acid is added to the strained latex. The rubber then coagulates (thickens) and rises to the surface in slabs. These slabs are removed and pressed to squeeze out remaining liquids and impurities. "Smoked sheet rubber" is then hung in a smoky atmosphere for a week to complete the drying and protect the rubber against molds (see MOLD). For "pale crepe rubber," the slabs are passed through rollers that cause the slabs to crinkle. The slabs are then hung and dried in heating rooms. For "crumb rubber," the slabs are run through machines that chop or shred them. The crumb rubber is then dried in hot air tunnels.

The rubber may undergo several processes on its way to being made into a product. These processes include adding pigment (coloring matter), adding ingredients that make the rubber softer and easier to shape, and shaping the product. Usually, the last process to be done is one called vulcanization. Vulcanization involves heating rubber with sulfur. This gives the rubber product more strength, hardness, and elasticity. Charles Goodyear, an American inventor, invented vulcanization in 1839 (see VULCANIZATION). Sometimes, vulcanization may occur at the same time as the shaping.

Variations in the ingredients and processes described above have resulted in a number of rubber derivatives, or special kinds of rubber. Rubber derivatives have certain qualities that are better than those of ordinary rubber. For example, they may be stronger or may resist abrasion better.

Following the development of vulcanization, toughened natural rubber found an early major use in rainwear and later in tires. After World War II (1939–1945), synthetic rubber came into wide use. Use of natural rubber continues to decrease in proportion to the use of synthetic rubber. However, despite the competition from synthetic rubber, natural rubber is still important. Natural rubber's resistance to heat buildup continues to be of value for tire treads on racing cars, buses, trucks, and airplanes. Scientific research has resulted in better growing, harvesting, and processing methods. The natural rubber industry, including the number of rubber plantations, continues to grow because the demand for rubber is so great.

Synthetic rubber The natural rubber industry was barely established when scientists began to search for methods of producing synthetic rubber. One of the first kinds of synthetic rubber, developed in Britain before 1900, was prepared from the hydrocarbon isoprene, which was obtained from

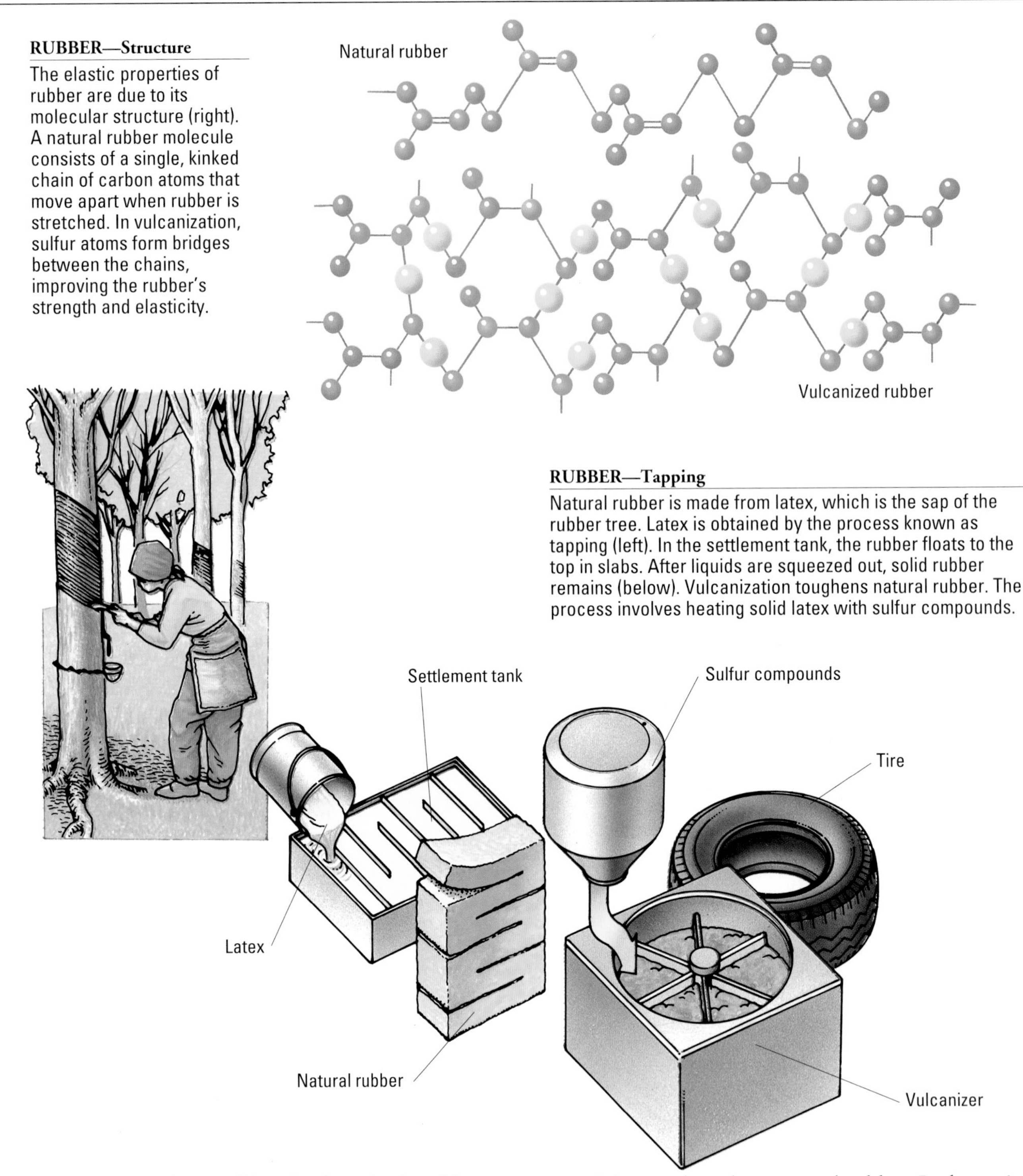

RUBBER—Structure

The elastic properties of rubber are due to its molecular structure (right). A natural rubber molecule consists of a single, kinked chain of carbon atoms that move apart when rubber is stretched. In vulcanization, sulfur atoms form bridges between the chains, improving the rubber's strength and elasticity.

RUBBER—Tapping

Natural rubber is made from latex, which is the sap of the rubber tree. Latex is obtained by the process known as tapping (left). In the settlement tank, the rubber floats to the top in slabs. After liquids are squeezed out, solid rubber remains (below). Vulcanization toughens natural rubber. The process involves heating solid latex with sulfur compounds.

turpentine. Almost all kinds of synthetic rubber are taken from products of the petroleum (oil) industry or of allied industries. The most important general-purpose synthetic rubber is the rubber known in the United States as SBR, an abbreviation for *styrene-butadiene rubber.* SBR has properties that are similar to those of natural rubber.

Chemists have continued to make better and better synthetic rubbers with many properties. For example, butyl rubber holds air and other gases much better than does natural rubber. It also resists aging, heat, and the effects of acids. Neoprene rubbers resist rough wear, oxygen, sunlight, gasoline, oil, and other chemicals. Nitrile rubber, also called Buna N, withstands heat up to 350°F [177°C] much better than natural rubber and most other synthetic rubbers can. Polysulfide rubbers have great resistance to softening and swelling in gasoline and greases. Polyurethane rubbers resist age and heat and withstand remarkable stresses and pressures. Silicone rubbers keep their rubberlike properties at much higher and lower temperatures than natural rubber or any other kind of synthetic rubber. Silicone rubbers can be used at temperatures ranging from -130°F to 600°F [-90°C to 316°C]. Fluorocarbon rubbers have tremendous resistance to petroleum-derived fluids and to high temperatures. Thermoplastic rubbers combine the strength of vulcanized rubber with the processing ability of plastics (see PLASTIC).

Cis-polyisoprene rubber may eliminate the reliance on plantations for natural rubber. Its chemical composition is almost the same as that of natural rubber. It works just as well as natural rubber for products such as heavy truck tires and heavy motor mountings. Improved systems have been developed to produce it.

RUBBER TREE The rubber tree is a tall, thin, tropical tree that belongs to the spurge family (see SPURGE FAMILY). The tree has dark, shiny leaves and yellow flowers. A white, milky fluid called latex flows through the cambium, just inside the bark (see CAMBIUM). This latex is the source of 99 percent of the world's natural rubber. The tree originally came from Brazil, but is now grown in many tropical areas, especially in southeast Asia. By careful breeding, scientists have been able to develop new varieties of rubber trees that produce much more latex than does the wild species.
See also BREEDING; RUBBER.

RUBBER TREE
Milky latex runs along a sloping groove cut into the bark of a rubber tree. The latex is being collected in a "cup" made from half a coconut shell.

RUBY Ruby is a red gemstone. It is a form of the mineral corundum. Sapphire is another color variety of this mineral (see CORUNDUM; SAPPHIRE). Corundum (aluminum oxide, Al_2O_3) is colorless when pure. A trace of chromium gives the mineral its red color. The most prized rubies have a deep, bluish red color known as pigeon's blood. They usually come from Myanmar (formerly Burma). Paler rubies come from Sri Lanka. Rubies from Thailand are often a yellowish red. Lower quality, small rubies have been found in North Carolina in the United States.

Large flawless rubies, especially of the pigeon's blood color, are extremely rare. They are the costliest of all gemstones. Such a ruby may be worth several times as much as a diamond of the same size (see DIAMOND).

Synthetic (human-made) rubies are common. They have the same hardness and composition as the real stone. Their cost can be quite low, but the production of synthetic rubies has in no way

RUBY
Rubies are valued for their beauty and rarity. They are a form of the mineral corundum, colored deep red by traces of chromium impurities. Rubies and diamonds, the other gemstones in this jewelry, are among the costliest of all gems.

destroyed the market for the natural ones. Experts can easily tell the difference between the synthetic product and the natural stone. Garnets are often sold under the misleading name of Arizona ruby or Cape ruby.
See also GARNET.

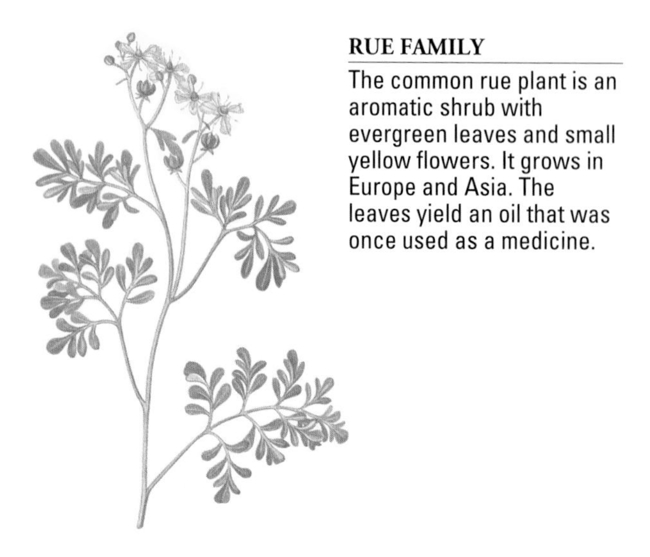

RUE FAMILY
The common rue plant is an aromatic shrub with evergreen leaves and small yellow flowers. It grows in Europe and Asia. The leaves yield an oil that was once used as a medicine.

RUE FAMILY The rue (ro͞o) family includes more than nine hundred species of herbaceous plants, shrubs, and trees (see HERBACEOUS PLANT). Most of these dicotyledons live in temperate and subtropical areas (see DICOTYLEDON). They have simple leaves or compound leaves made of several leaflets (see LEAF). The leaves usually have small, colorless glands that, when crushed, give off a sweet fragrance. The flowers are usually scented and grow in clusters. The rue plant is one of about forty perennial shrubs belonging to the genus *Ruta* (see PERENNIAL PLANT). The most important members of this family belong to genus *Citrus.*
See also CITRUS FRUIT.

RUMINANT (ro͞o′mə nənt) The ruminants are hoofed mammals that chew cud (partly digested food) (see MAMMAL). Ruminants belong to the suborder Ruminantia. This suborder includes six living families and three extinct ones. Ruminants have no incisors (front teeth) in the upper jaw. Ruminants chew their food and cud with their large flat cheek teeth, or molars (see TEETH). Familiar ruminants include antelopes, camels, cattle, deer, giraffes, goats, llamas, and sheep.

The stomachs of most ruminants have four chambers, the first and biggest of which is the rumen, or paunch. In an adult cow, this may have a capacity of over 264 qt. [250 liters]. Food passes into the rumen after little or no chewing, and

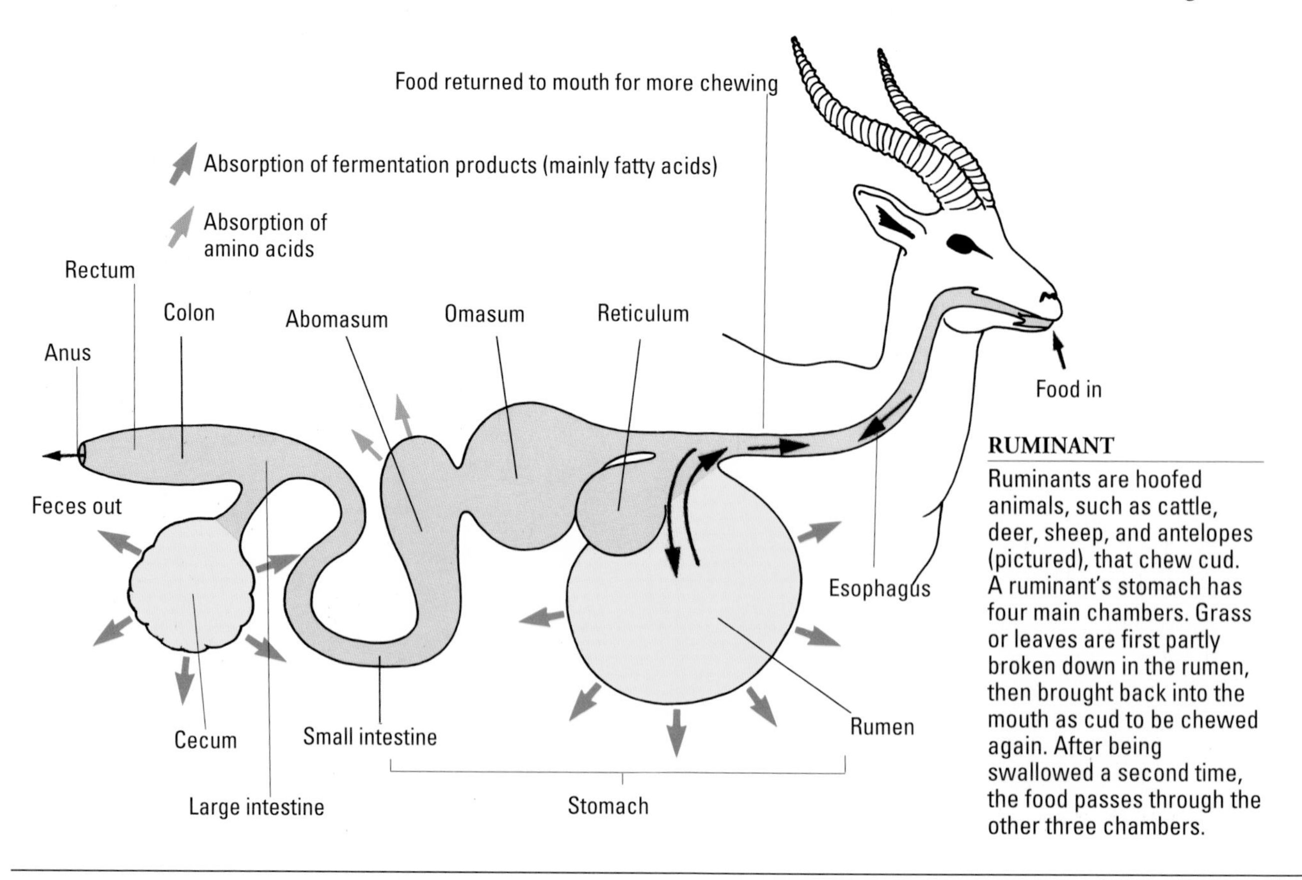

RUMINANT
Ruminants are hoofed animals, such as cattle, deer, sheep, and antelopes (pictured), that chew cud. A ruminant's stomach has four main chambers. Grass or leaves are first partly broken down in the rumen, then brought back into the mouth as cud to be chewed again. After being swallowed a second time, the food passes through the other three chambers.

bacteria living in the rumen begin to break the food down or ferment it (see BACTERIA; FERMENTATION). Some time later, often while lying down in a safe place, the animal brings the softened food, now known as cud, back into its mouth for a thorough chewing. When it is well mixed with saliva, the food is swallowed again, but this time it bypasses the rumen and goes into the second chamber—the reticulum. Here the breakdown, or digestion, is carried on by more bacteria, and the food passes on to the omasum. This is the third chamber of the stomach, and its main job is to absorb water from the food. In the fourth chamber, called the abomasum, the food is mixed with a variety of digestive juices. It then passes into the small intestine, and digestion is completed in the normal way (see ALIMENTARY CANAL; DIGESTIVE SYSTEM).

The grass and other plants eaten by the ruminants consist largely of cellulose, which is very tough and difficult for animals to digest (see CELLULOSE). The numerous bacteria in the rumen and reticulum carry out the early stages of digestion and ensure that the ruminants get as much nutrient from their food as possible.

RUSH Rush is the common name for about three hundred species of herbaceous plants that belong to genus *Juncus* of the rush family, Juncaceae (see HERBACEOUS PLANT). Most of these grasslike monocotyledons grow in damp grassland marshes in temperate areas (see MONOCOTYLEDON). They have round green stems and spikes or clusters of tiny, greenish brown flowers (see INFLORESCENCE). Some rushes have leaves in the form of brown scales at the base of the stems, but others have long, needlelike leaves. These leaves are often used for weaving mats, chair seats, and baskets.

RUSH
Rush is a grasslike plant that grows in damp places or, as seen here, among sand dunes on the seashore.

Some plants that are called rushes are not true rushes at all. For example, scouring rush is a horsetail, and bulrush is a sedge.
See also HORSETAIL; SEDGE FAMILY.

RUST Rust is a brownish red substance that forms on the surfaces of iron and steel when these metals are exposed to damp air. Rust is a hydrated (water-containing) form of iron oxide, with the formula $3Fe_2O_3 \cdot H_2O$.

Rusting occurs when the oxygen in the air unites with iron in a process known as oxidation (see CORROSION; OXIDATION AND REDUCTION). However, rusting is not only a process of oxidation, because the presence of moisture is also necessary to produce the change. The complex rusting process is speeded up by the presence of salts and acids. Rusting is therefore more severe in coastal regions and in industrial areas where the air may contain acidic sulfur dioxide fumes (see POLLUTION).

Rust not only corrodes the surface. It also weakens the metal. A lengthy exposure to air and moisture causes nails to rust away and holes to form in sheet iron.

If the rust has not been forming for too long a time, it can be removed by scrubbing with water or using a polishing powder. To remove a thick coat of rust, a hard abrasive, such as a grindstone or file, is needed.

To prevent rust, iron or steel may be coated with paint, plastic, or a corrosion-resistant metal such as tin or zinc. Chemically coated paper wrapped around metal objects also prevents rust. The metal may also be alloyed with a corrosion-resistant metal or mixture of metals, such as nickel and chromium (see ALLOY). The alloys produced, often called stainless steels, are highly resistant to corrosion.
See also STAINLESS STEEL.

RUST AND SMUT Rusts and smuts are plant diseases caused by various types of parasitic fungi (plural of *fungus*) (see FUNGUS; PARASITE). The fungi themselves are also referred to as rusts and smuts. There are more than four thousand species of fungi that cause rusts. Most rusts have life cycles with two to five stages, each of which produces a different kind of spore (see SPORE). Usually, at least one of these stages produces brownish spores that look like powdery iron rust. Some rusts go through all of their life stages on one host. These rusts are said to be autoecious. Other rusts alternate between two hosts, spending one or more life stages on each. These rusts are said to be heteroecious. For example, a common rust that affects wheat spends the winter as a parasite on barberry. Sometimes, heteroecious rusts can be controlled by killing or removing the alternate host.

There are more than a thousand different fungi that cause smuts. Smuts produce large numbers of dark brown or black spores. These spores are usually contained within blisters in seeds, stems, leaves, flowers, or bulbs.

Both rusts and smuts send special rootlike structures called haustoria into the host (see HAUSTORIA). These haustoria absorb nutrients from the cells of the plant host. This often causes the infected cells to wither and die. Rusts and smuts cause a great deal of damage to cereal crops throughout the world (see CEREAL CROP). They can be controlled by fungicides or crop rotation (see AGRICULTURE; FUNGICIDE). Frequently, all the infected plants must be destroyed to prevent the disease from spreading. Scientists are constantly trying to breed new varieties of plants that are resistant to these fungi.

See also BREEDING.

RUST AND SMUT

These leaves are infected by a rust fungus. Such parasitic fungi cause widespread damage to crops throughout the world. They can be controlled by fungicides or crop rotation.

RUTHERFORD, ERNEST (1871–1937) Ernest Rutherford was a British physicist. He was born in New Zealand and, in 1895, won a scholarship to Cambridge University, England. He eventually became head of the Cavendish Laboratory at Cambridge.

At Cambridge, Rutherford began his study of radioactivity (see RADIOACTIVITY). He found that there were different kinds of rays given off by radioactive substances. He called some alpha rays and others beta rays. These names are still used. Since these rays actually consist of particles, they are also called alpha and beta particles (see ALPHA PARTICLE; BETA PARTICLE). The alpha particles have a positive electric charge and are made up of two neutrons and two protons bound together. Beta particles are streams of electrons. Rutherford also studied the structure of the atom. He found that most of the mass (weight) is in the tiny nucleus. The electrons are very light, carry a negative charge, and are spread in a kind of cloud around the nucleus. Rutherford is responsible for naming the proton, one of the particles in the nucleus (see ATOM; ELECTRON; NUCLEUS; PROTON).

Rutherford was also the first person to change one element into another one. He changed nitrogen into oxygen by bombarding the nitrogen atoms with alpha particles (see TRANSMUTATION OF ELEMENTS). Rutherford was a dedicated scientist and worked tirelessly to understand how things actually happened. His brilliant work gained him many honors. In 1908, he was awarded the Nobel Prize for chemistry.

RUTILE (ro͞o′tēl′) Rutile is a variety of titanium oxide. It is the main ore from which titanium is extracted (see TITANIUM). Rutile is usually found as crystals and occurs in several kinds of rocks containing quartz, such as gneiss and schist. It is also found in grains in sediments, particularly sands (see ROCK). The smaller crystals are usually light brown in color. The larger crystals are usually black but may be blue, violet, or yellow. Rutile is mined in Australia, Brazil, India, and the United States.

RYE (rī) Rye is a cereal crop that belongs to the grass family (see CEREAL CROP; GRASS). This annual plant grows in temperate areas throughout the Northern Hemisphere (see ANNUAL PLANT). It can be cultivated further north than any other cereal and also grows on poorer soils. Rye grows to a height of almost 6.6 ft. [2 m]. Its grains (fruits) grow in thin spikes.

Almost half the world's supply of rye is grown in the former Soviet Union. Only about 2 percent comes from the United States. Rye is used to make flour and certain alcoholic beverages. Rye is high in carbohydrates. It provides lesser amounts of protein, potassium, and B vitamins. Rye is often affected by ergot fungus. Ergot destroys the grains and, if eaten, causes a type of insanity called ergotism, or St. Anthony's fire.

See also FUNGUS.

RYE

Rye is an important food crop, especially in regions with a cool climate and poor soil.

S

SABIN, ALBERT BRUCE (1906–1993) (sā' bĭn, ăl'bərt brōōs) Albert Sabin was an American doctor and biologist who developed a vaccine for the disease polio (see POLIO MYELITIS; VACCINATION). Sabin was born at Bialystok in Russia, which is now part of Poland. He became an American citizen in 1930. Sabin began studying dentistry at New York University but later changed to medicine. He became professor of pediatrics at the University of Cincinnati College of Medicine in 1939 and continued teaching for over thirty years.

In treating children's diseases, Sabin saw many cases of polio. After the end of World War II (1939–1945), he began research into a way of preventing this crippling viral disease (see VIRUS). One method of preventing disease is vaccination. Jonas Salk had developed a polio vaccine that used dead viruses (see SALK, JONAS EDWARD). Sabin wanted to find a way of using live viruses, which he thought would be more powerful.

Sabin eventually managed to breed a kind of polio virus that was too weak to cause serious disease. It still caused the production of antibodies, however. These antibodies made a person who had taken the vaccine immune to any other polio infection (see ANTIBODY; IMMUNITY; INFECTION).

Sabin's vaccine was first used on a large scale in the United States in 1960. The Sabin vaccine is sometimes given on a lump of sugar or as a small dose of liquid in a spoon. Thus, immunization is fast and painless. The Sabin vaccine is different from the Salk vaccine, which has to be injected. During his career, Sabin received numerous honorary degrees and awards for his contributions to the field of medicine. He died in March 1993 in Washington, D.C.

See also DISEASE; INJECTION.

SABIN, FLORENCE (1871–1953) (sā' bĭn, flôr' əns) Florence Sabin was an American medical doctor, teacher, and scientist. Sabin is best known for her studies of the blood, the lymphatic system, and the disease tuberculosis (see BLOOD; LYMPHATIC

SYSTEM; TUBERCULOSIS). She is also noted for being the first woman to teach at Johns Hopkins Medical College in Baltimore, Maryland.

Sabin was born in Central City, Colorado. She earned a bachelor's degree in science and mathematics at Smith College in Northampton, Massachusetts. In 1896, she entered Johns Hopkins. While still a student, she constructed a model of and wrote about the brain. Her model and writings later were turned into a widely used textbook. Sabin began teaching anatomy at Johns Hopkins in 1901. There, she studied the blood and the lymphatic system. She also studied the body's immunity by observing white blood cells (see IMMUNITY). She developed a method of studying living cells by staining them with dye and then looking at them under a microscope. The dye highlighted certain features of the cells.

Sabin's teachings had a long-lasting effect on the medical community. For twenty years, every freshman at Johns Hopkins was required to take the anatomy course she taught. In 1925, she became the first woman elected to the National Academy of Sciences. The academy conducts scientific research and also advises the government about scientific matters. She also became the first woman member of the Rockefeller Institute for Medical Research, now Rockefeller University. She spent thirteen years there conducting investigations on tuberculosis. Sabin retired from the institute in 1938 and moved back to Colorado. There, she became politically active in the effort to upgrade public health. As a result of the movement, new health laws were passed, and higher health standards were established in Colorado. Sabin is credited with helping change the purpose of medical study from curing disease to preventing it by maintaining good health.

SABLE The sable is a graceful mammal belonging to the weasel family, Mustelidae, and related to the marten (see MARTEN; WEASEL). The sable is found in the forests of northern Asia. The sable lives alone, usually in trees. The animal feeds on birds and other small animals, such as squirrels and other rodents. It also eats eggs.

The females have an especially long gestation period, lasting about 300 days (see GESTATION PERIOD). At the end of this period, the sable gives birth to one to five young.

This animal ranges from about 13 to 20 in. [32 to 51 cm] in length, not including the tail. The color of the sable's body varies from brown to almost black. Some sables have dusky or salmon-colored throat patches. The sable's fur is highly prized, being used for jackets, collars, coats, and stoles. Sables have been hunted and trapped for centuries.

SALAMANDER (săl′ə măn′dər) A salamander is a type of amphibian that usually has a long, wide tail (see AMPHIBIAN). There are about 300 species of salamanders. Many salamanders belong to the family Salamandridae, which also contains the newts (see NEWT).

Salamanders vary in length from about 1.6 in. [4 cm] to about 5 ft. [1.5 m], but most are 4 to 6 in. [10 to 15 cm] long. The bodies of salamanders are usually long and slender, with a long tail about the same width as the body. Salamanders have four short legs and a small, smooth head. Their skin is smooth, slippery, and often colorful.

SALAMANDER—Fire salamander

The fire salamander is one of many species of salamanders that live in the eastern United States.

SALAMANDER—Skin

The red salamander (top) burrows into the muddy banks of streams. Like most salamanders, it has a smooth skin. Tylotriton (bottom) is unusual because it has warty skin.

Most salamanders hatch from eggs in the water. They begin life as larvae (plural of *larva*) swimming in water (see LARVA). The larvae change into adult salamanders, which spend most of their time on land (see METAMORPHOSIS). However, some salamanders give birth to well-developed tadpoles. All salamanders must stay near water or in a moist area because they breathe through their skin. To be able to do this, they must keep their skin wet.

SALINITY (sə lĭn′ĭ tē) Salinity refers to the concentration of salt in a body of water. Salinity depends on the amount of fresh water that flows into the body of water and on the amount of evaporation that occurs from the body of water (see EVAPORATION). For example, the Baltic Sea has many rivers flowing into it, plentiful rain and snow, and a low rate of evaporation. Consequently, the water is fresher than that of most other seas and oceans. On the other hand, the Red Sea has fewer rivers flowing into it and a high rate of evaporation. As a result, it has a high salinity.

Inland lakes in dry, hot regions often have extremely high salinity. For example, the Great Salt Lake in Utah is so named because it is very salty. Its salt content is four to five times higher than that of the oceans. Lake Van in Turkey, another inland lake, has a salinity of 33 percent. Ocean water, in comparison, has a salinity of 3.3 to 3.7 percent.

ACTIVITY *How to test salinity*

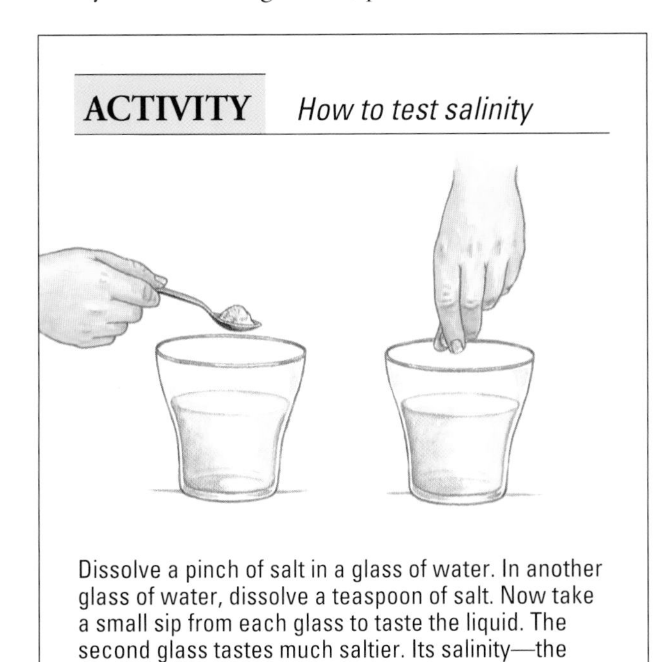

Dissolve a pinch of salt in a glass of water. In another glass of water, dissolve a teaspoon of salt. Now take a small sip from each glass to taste the liquid. The second glass tastes much saltier. Its salinity—the proportion of salt to water—is much higher.

SALIVA (sə lī′və) Saliva is a watery, colorless fluid produced by the salivary glands in the mouth. Saliva is very important in the digestion of food. It contains some mucus and enzymes and an alkaline, or acid-neutralizing, chemical (see ACID; DIGESTIVE SYSTEM; ENZYME; GLAND; MUCUS).

Saliva contains the enzyme ptyalin, or salivary amylase, which helps break down starches into sugars. This is the first step in the digestion of carbohydrates (see CARBOHYDRATE).

The flow of saliva is greatly increased by chewing food. Saliva helps lubricate the food for its passage down the esophagus, the tube that leads to the stomach. Saliva also keeps the mouth moist for comfort.

SALK, JONAS EDWARD (1914–) (sôk, jō′ nəs ĕd′ wərd) Jonas Salk is an American doctor and biologist who developed the first vaccine for the viral disease polio (see POLIO MYELITIS; VACCINATION; VIRUS). Salk made his vaccine using dead polio viruses. He managed to kill the virus in such a way that it still caused the production of antibodies in a person's body (see ANTIBODY; IMMUNITY). This meant that a person who was immunized with the vaccine would not get polio. Salk's vaccine was first used in 1955. Five years later, another type of polio vaccine, developed by Albert Sabin, came into use (see SABIN, ALBERT BRUCE). Salk's and Sabin's vaccines have almost wiped out what was once a common and terrible disease of childhood.

SALMON (săm'ən) A salmon is a fish that belongs to the family Salmonidae. It is closely related to the trout (see TROUT). Most species of salmon hatch in freshwater streams but move to the ocean as they mature.

Young salmon grow up in the stream in which they were hatched. As they mature, they go through three stages—fry, parr, and smolt. The smolts begin the downstream migration to the sea (see MIGRATION). Salmon live in the ocean for one to four years. During this period, they grow very quickly.

When salmon are ready to spawn (reproduce), they return to the same stream they left years before (see SPAWNING). Biologists think that the fish recognize the streams by their smell. After the salmon reach their streams, they swim up to the cold, clear headwaters (source) to spawn. Sometimes, the salmon must leap small waterfalls and swim in powerful rapids to reach their goal. Salmon are very strong swimmers. After they spawn in the gravel bottom of the streams, most salmon die. However, some Atlantic salmon are able to return to the sea, where they recover their strength, and then go upstream to spawn a second time.

Some species of salmon do not go out to sea. They stay in fresh water all their lives. These so-called landlocked salmon are usually found in cold, clear, deep lakes.

There are seven species of salmon in the world. All of them are found in the northern part of the Northern Hemisphere. Six live in the Pacific region, and one lives in the Atlantic. The largest species is the chinook salmon, which commonly reaches a length of 38 in. [97 cm] and weighs 40 lb. [18 kg], although it can be much bigger.

People all over the world rely on salmon as a source of protein. Salmon are also a highly prized game fish. Some sports fishers travel thousands of miles to fish for salmon.

The numbers of wild salmon are declining, partly because of overfishing. In addition, the construction of dams has prevented many salmon from swimming up streams to spawn. Water pollution has also killed many salmon (see POLLUTION). Fishways—structures that allow fish to swim around dams—have been built around many dams (see DAM). This has saved or restored the salmon to many streams. During the 1970s, much progress was made in bringing salmon back to streams in New England, from which they had disappeared years before. The numbers of Pacific salmon continue to decline, however. Most of the salmon eaten today are reared on fish farms.

SALMONELLA Salmonella are a group of bacteria. The most important are those that cause typhoid (*Salmonella typhimurium*), paratyphoid (*Salmonella paratyphi*) and food poisoning (various species) (see FOOD POISONING; TYPHOID FEVER). Those causing typhoid and paratyphoid are rarely found in areas with good sanitation, but those causing food poisoning are widely distributed in nature, and are most likely to be found on raw

SALMON

Although most salmon (left) live in the oceans, they spawn (reproduce) in freshwater streams. Salmon make their way upstream to the place of their birth to spawn. They may even have to leap waterfalls to reach their destination.

meat, eggs, and poultry. The bacteria grow very rapidly in warm, moist conditions. They can be transferred easily onto food by insects or during food preparation. Food must be handled properly to avoid contamination. Thorough cooking kills the bacteria, and refrigerating or freezing food stops them from growing.

SALTPETER Saltpeter, or niter, is a naturally occurring form of potassium nitrate (KNO_3). It forms in the ground when bacteria break down plant remains. Saltpeter is a valuable fertilizer, supplying both nitrogen and potassium for growing plants (see FERTILIZER). Saltpeter is also used in manufacturing enamels and glass and in processing meat. When mixed with carbon and sulfur, it forms gunpowder.

Sodium nitrate is called Chile saltpeter. It is found in large deposits in northern Chile, together with potassium nitrate. Calcium nitrate is called Norway saltpeter. Both Chile and Norway saltpeter are good fertilizers.

See also NITRATE.

SALTS In science, the term *salt* applies to a substance produced by the reaction of an acid and a base. The reaction between an acid and a base is a neutralization reaction. Most often, an acid and a base react to give a salt plus water (see ACID; BASE; NEUTRALIZATION).

Most salts are crystalline structures, such as common table salt (sodium chloride). Sodium chloride is formed by the reaction of hydrochloric acid (an acid) and sodium hydroxide (a base). This reaction produces sodium chloride and water:

$$HCl + NaOH \rightarrow NaCl + H_2O$$

A salt consists of positive ions from a base and negative ions from an acid (see IONS AND IONIZATION). When in solution or the molten (melted) state, most salts are completely dissociated into negative ions and positive ions. For this reason, salts are good electrical conductors.

See also CONDUCTION OF ELECTRICITY; SOLUTION AND SOLUBILITY.

SAN ANDREAS FAULT The San Andreas fault is a break in the earth's crust near the California coast (see FAULT). It runs northwestward from the Gulf of California to the Pacific Ocean near San Francisco.

According to the theory of plate tectonics, the earth's crust is divided into a number of moving plates (see PLATE TECTONICS). The San Andreas fault is thought to be the edge between the eastern Pacific plate and the North American plate. Geologists estimate that the area west of the fault has moved horizontally northwestward about 200 mi. [320 km] over the last 15 million years. In 1906, a sudden movement of the plate caused the catastrophic San Francisco earthquake. In this earthquake, the plates moved 21 ft. [6.4 m]. However, the San Andreas fault was not the cause of the 1989 earthquake in San Francisco. This earthquake was caused by movement along one of the many faults that branch off the San Andreas fault.

Many people live near the San Andreas fault. Seismologists are involved in intensive research along the fault in hope of preventing—or at least predicting—future earthquakes.

See also EARTHQUAKE; SEISMOLOGY.

SAND Sand is tiny particles of rocks and minerals with diameters ranging from 0.0025 to 0.08 in. [0.06 to 2.0 mm]. Sand is one of the three main kinds of particles in soil. The most common mineral found in sand is quartz (see MINERAL; QUARTZ; ROCK; SOIL). Other important components of sand include garnet, zircon, and rutile. Some beach sands are made from fragments of seashells or coral reef material.

Sand comes in a variety of colors. The presence of small quantities of iron oxide gives sand a yellow or red appearance. Black sand is colored by grains of basalt, a rock of volcanic origin that contains many dark minerals. Green sand, which is widespread on the ocean floor, gets its color from the mineral glauconite.

Most of the world's large sand deposits occur on seashores, along rivers and lakes, and in deserts. The way sand forms helps explain why this is true.

The sand-making process begins when rock material is worn away by erosion (see EROSION). In a river, this material becomes rounded because the particles are constantly rubbing against each other as they move downstream. When the sand particles reach a lake or the sea, they are washed about by the waves and currents. Eventually, most of the sand accumulates on beaches. There, it is further rounded by the pounding waves.

In deserts, sand is transported and rounded by the wind. Desert sand probably originated from ancient deposits of sand that formed in some earlier geological time period. The shifting desert sands may form great crescent-shaped dunes, which point in the direction of their movement (see DUNE).

People have developed many uses for sand. In the building industry, sand is an important ingredient in cement, concrete, and glass. Sand is also used as an abrasive (see ABRASIVE). Many cities purify their water by filtering it through sand. Some sand contains valuable materials such as gold, platinum, and diamonds.

PROJECT 21

SANDALWOOD
The Haleakala sandalwood has leathery leaves and red buds that open to reveal pale yellow flowers. It grows in Hawaii.

SANDALWOOD Sandalwood is the name given to twenty-five species of trees belonging to genus *Santalum*. They are native to southeastern Asia and to the islands of the South Pacific. The most common species of sandalwood tree is the white sandalwood. This tree grows to a height of

SAND
Sand varies widely in color. Coarse brown sand (above), known as sharp sand, is used in the construction industry. Some beach sands (top right) are pale colored or even white. Desert sands (bottom right) are often reddish in color, due to the presence of traces of iron oxide.

about 33 ft. [10 m]. It has thick leaves and clusters of red, ball-shaped flowers. Its scented wood is used in furniture and for carving. The wood yields a strong oil that is used in soap, candles, incense, and perfumes.

SAND AND SHOT BLASTING Sand and shot blasting are industrial methods of cleaning the surfaces of materials such as metal, stone, and brick. Both methods work by directing a high-pressure stream of sand or other abrasive particles at the surface. When the sand is wet, the process is known as mud blasting.

Such processes of blasting are particularly valuable because the abrasive material can often be reused many times. When the work is done in a closed chamber, the abrasive can be collected after use. The abrasive materials are funneled into a collecting chamber and, if necessary, prepared for reuse. For outside work, however, the abrasive materials usually cannot be recovered.

Machines that have a rapidly rotating wheel or disk to hurl abrasives (such as steel shot) are also used to clean surfaces. Manufacturers use this method because it is faster and often less costly than sandblasting.

See also ABRASIVE; SAND.

SAND DOLLAR Sand dollars are very flat sea urchins, belonging to phylum Echinodermata (see ECHINODERMATA; SEA URCHIN). Sand dollars usually live in warm, shallow ocean waters.

The sand dollar has a hollow, shell-like skeleton called a test. The test is covered with tiny spines, which are used in burrowing. The upper surface of the test has holes, arranged in a flower or star pattern, through which the sand dollar can extend its tube feet. These organs are used for breathing. The tube feet on the lower surface are also used for movement and to help bring food toward the mouth, which is in the center of the lower surface.

When covered by the tide, a sand dollar positions itself on its edge, about half-buried in the sand. It sweeps plankton and other tiny floating organisms into its mouth (see PLANKTON). If an enemy, such as a starfish or a mollusk, approaches,

SAND DOLLAR

A sand dollar is a type of flat sea urchin with very short spines covering its shell-like skeleton.

the sand dollar quickly buries itself in the sand. It also hides in the sand at low tide.

SANDSTONE Sandstone is a sedimentary rock composed of sand-sized particles cemented together (see SEDIMENTARY ROCK). The grains range in diameter from 0.003 to 0.08 in. [0.06 to 2.0 mm].

There are many different types of sandstone. They differ according to the type of sand, the cementing material, and the impurities found in the rock. Sandstone that contains quartz sand cemented by silica is called quartzite. Quartzite is harder than sandstones that have iron oxides or lime as their cementing material. Many sandstones

SANDSTONE

This sandstone column once formed part of a seashore cliff, where it was eroded by the action of the sea.

are red or brown because they contain iron oxides either as cement or as impurities. Red sandstones are made from sands laid down in ancient deserts. Sandstones made from river sands usually show marks from the river current. Those from ancient beaches may have ripple marks in them.

Sandstone is an important building material. Huge quantities of sandstone are quarried in the United States, especially in Ohio, Connecticut, and the upper Mississippi River valley.

See also SAND.

SAP Sap is a watery liquid found in the xylem and phloem of vascular plants (see PHLOEM; VASCULAR PLANT; XYLEM). Sap in the xylem contains dissolved minerals, which are transported from the roots to the leaves of the plant. This sap provides some of the raw materials needed for producing food in the process of photosynthesis (see PHOTOSYNTHESIS). Sap in the phloem contains dissolved food. This food is produced in the leaves through photosynthesis. Sap contains a lot of sugar. The sap in the phloem is thicker, or more syrupy, than the sap in the xylem.

Maple syrup is made from sap of the maple tree, which is boiled for hours to concentrate the sugar (see MAPLE FAMILY). Natural rubber comes from latex, a milky juice that is not a true sap, formed in rubber trees and some other plants (see RUBBER TREE).

SAPPHIRE (săf′ĭr′) A sapphire is a transparent gem composed of the mineral corundum (aluminum oxide, Al_2O_3) (see CORUNDUM; MINERAL; PRECIOUS STONE AND GEM). Corundum is found in a variety of colors. The gems called rubies are composed of red corundum (see RUBY). All other colors of gem-quality corundum are called sapphire. Colorless gems of pure corundum are called white sapphire. True sapphire is blue, ranging from a very pale blue to indigo. The color is due mainly to the presence of small amounts of iron and titanium.

Gem-quality corundum may also contain small amounts of other substances that color the mineral. These colored gems are often named after other gems, with the prefix *oriental.* For example, oriental topaz is yellow, oriental amethyst is violet, and oriental emerald is green. Much sapphire is unevenly colored. Its color also changes with the direction of view.

Sapphires can be found in many igneous rocks and also in schists (see IGNEOUS ROCK; SCHIST). The best-known deposits in the United States are in Montana and North Carolina. Sapphire deposits are also found in Kashmir, Sri Lanka, Myanmar (formerly Burma), Thailand, Australia, India, and South Africa.

Gem cutters usually cut transparent sapphires so that they are faceted. This means that they cut many flat surfaces onto the gem, giving it a great deal of sparkle. Star sapphire and other nontransparent varieties of sapphires are usually rounded and polished rather than faceted.

Synthetic (human-made) sapphires have been produced since the early 1900s. The synthetic gems greatly resemble the natural ones, and it is difficult for an untrained person to tell the difference. Besides being used for jewelry, synthetic sapphires are also used in cutting tools and as a high-grade abrasive.

See also ABRASIVE.

SAPPHIRE

Sapphire is a form of the mineral corundum. It gets its blue color from traces of iron and titanium impurities.

SAPROPHYTE
Saprophytes, such as the bracket fungi growing on the fallen log (left), are organisms that feed on dead organic (carbon-containing) material. Most saprophytes cannot make their own food by photosynthesis.

SAPROPHYTE (săp′rə fīt′) A saprophyte is an organism that feeds on dead organic (carbon-containing) material. By digesting and absorbing nutrients from this material, saprophytes play an important part in the process of decay (see FOOD CHAIN). Most saprophytes are fungi and bacteria that contain no chlorophyll. These organisms cannot make their own food by photosynthesis (see BACTERIA; CHLOROPHYLL; FUNGUS; PHOTOSYNTHESIS). Some flowering plants are also saprophytes. Most of these plants, however, rely on fungi on their roots called mycorrhizae to process and release nutrients from decaying organisms. Then the plant can absorb the nutrients into its roots.

SAPSUCKER A sapsucker is a bird that belongs to the woodpecker family, Picidae. Sapsuckers are found only in North America. The yellow-bellied sapsucker is found throughout most of eastern North America. It grows to a length of 7.75 in. [19 cm]. Two similar species are the red-breasted and red-naped sapsuckers. These three species of sapsuckers are boldly colored birds. Williamson's sapsucker lives in the western part of the continent. It grows to a length of 8.25 in. [20.6 cm]. It is similar in color to the other sapsuckers, but it does not have red on the head.

Sapsuckers drill rows of holes into a tree with their bills. Sap from the trees eventually begins to ooze out of these holes (see SAP). The sapsuckers return later to eat the sap and the many small insects that get stuck in it.

SAPSUCKER
High-speed photography has captured a picture of this yellow-bellied sapsucker as it arrives at its nest with a beakful of insects.

SAPWOOD Sapwood forms the outer part of a tree trunk. It is the region of the xylem that carries water and dissolved minerals from the roots to the leaves (see XYLEM). Sapwood is lighter in color and also less dense than the heartwood in the center of the trunk (see HEARTWOOD). A new ring of sapwood grows under the bark each year, forming a new annual ring and increasing the girth (distance around) of the trunk (see ANNUAL RING). Healthy trees add about 1 in. [2.54 cm] to their girth every year. As more sapwood is added to the outer part of

...unk, the inner layers of sapwood are crushed. ...s of the sapwood become filled with various ...anic (carbon-containing) compounds and are gradually changed into heartwood.

SARDINE (sär dēn′) A sardine is a small saltwater fish that belongs to the herring family, Clupeidae. It is a slender, silvery fish that swims in large schools (groups) of thousands of fish. Although there are over seventeen species of these small saltwater herrings, only five species called sardines are found off the coasts of North America.

Sardines eat small organisms called plankton, which float in the water (see PLANKTON). The sardines, in turn, are eaten by many fishes and birds (see FOOD CHAIN).

Sardines are caught in large numbers by commercial fishers. They are canned and sold as food for people. In Europe, the name *sardine* is also given to pilchards.

SARGASSO (sär găs′ō) *Sargasso* is a genus of algae found in the ocean (see ALGAE). The sargasso algae are brown with long stems; flat, leaflike parts; and many small structures called air bladders. The air bladders allow the sargasso to float in large, thick, flat bunches. There is a fish—called the sargasso fish—that very closely resembles a piece of sargasso alga (singular of *algae*). The fish hides in the algae and is very hard to see (see CAMOUFLAGE; PROTECTIVE COLORATION). There is an area in the southern part of the North Atlantic Ocean that is called the Sargasso Sea because the sargasso algae are so abundant there.

SASSAFRAS (săs′ə frăs′) The sassafras is a small deciduous tree that is found in the eastern part of the United States. It belongs to the laurel family, Lauraceae (see LAUREL). It usually does not grow taller than 40 ft. [12 m], although some specimens reach about 100 ft. [30 m]. The leaves are irregularly shaped with one, two, or three lobes (see LEAF). In the fall, the sassafras leaves adapt brilliant red and gold colors. The tree also produces small black or dark blue berries. These berries are eaten by many types of wildlife. A pleasant-smelling oil is obtained from sassafras roots and wood. The oil is used to flavor candy, tea, and other beverages.

SASSAFRAS

Sassafras, a plant of the laurel family, has lobed leaves (top). Sassafras trees (above) rarely grow more than 40 ft. [12 m] tall. An oil extracted from the wood and roots is used as a flavoring in food and beverages.

SATELLITE

A satellite (săt′l īt′) is an object that orbits another, larger body. A satellite is either natural or artificial. A natural satellite generally is a celestial object, such as a moon, that orbits a planet (see MOON; ORBIT; PLANET). An artificial satellite is made by humans and is launched into orbit around planets, such as Earth. Artificial satellites perform various tasks, including transmitting radio, telephone, and television signals; sending back information helpful for weather forecasting, navigation, or military surveillance; and sending back scientific information about the earth and space.

Natural satellites In the solar system, all the planets except Mercury and Venus have at least one moon (see SOLAR SYSTEM). One of Jupiter's moons, Ganymede, is the largest satellite known to orbit any planet. It is larger than Mercury. The earth's moon is about one fourth the size of the earth.

Astronomers probably have not discovered all the moons in the solar system (see ASTRONOMY). So far, astronomers have discovered the following numbers of moons for each of the planets: Mars, two; Jupiter, sixteen; Saturn, twenty-three; Uranus, fifteen; Neptune, eight; and Pluto, one.

SEASAT

Seasat was a satellite launched by NASA in 1978. It used radar signals that were bounced off the surface of the ocean to plot a map showing the shape of the seabed. These results were transmitted by radio to a receiving station on the ground.

Some moons are made of materials that are similar to the materials that make up the planet they orbit. Other moons are composed of materials that differ significantly from the planet. Most moons orbit in the same direction as the planet. However, at least two moons—Saturn's Phoebe and Neptune's Triton—orbit in the opposite direction. Most moons orbit in or near the plane of the planet's equator (an imaginary line running around the middle of the planet).

Space probes have helped astronomers learn more about the outer planets and their satellites. Space probes launched by the United States in 1977 *(Voyager 1* and *Voyager 2)* passed near Jupiter in 1979, Uranus in 1986, and Neptune in 1989 (see SPACE EXPLORATION).

Artificial satellites In 1687, the English scientist Sir Isaac Newton suggested the possibility of placing an artificial satellite in orbit (see NEWTON, SIR ISAAC). However, it was not until the mid-1900s that rocket technology had advanced to the point that people were able to launch satellites (see ROCKET). The former Soviet Union launched the first artificial satellite, *Sputnik 1,* in 1957 (see SPUTNIK). The United States launched its first artificial satellite, *Explorer I,* in 1958.

Since that time, many other countries have launched satellites of their own, including Australia, Britain, Canada, China, France, Germany, India, and Italy.

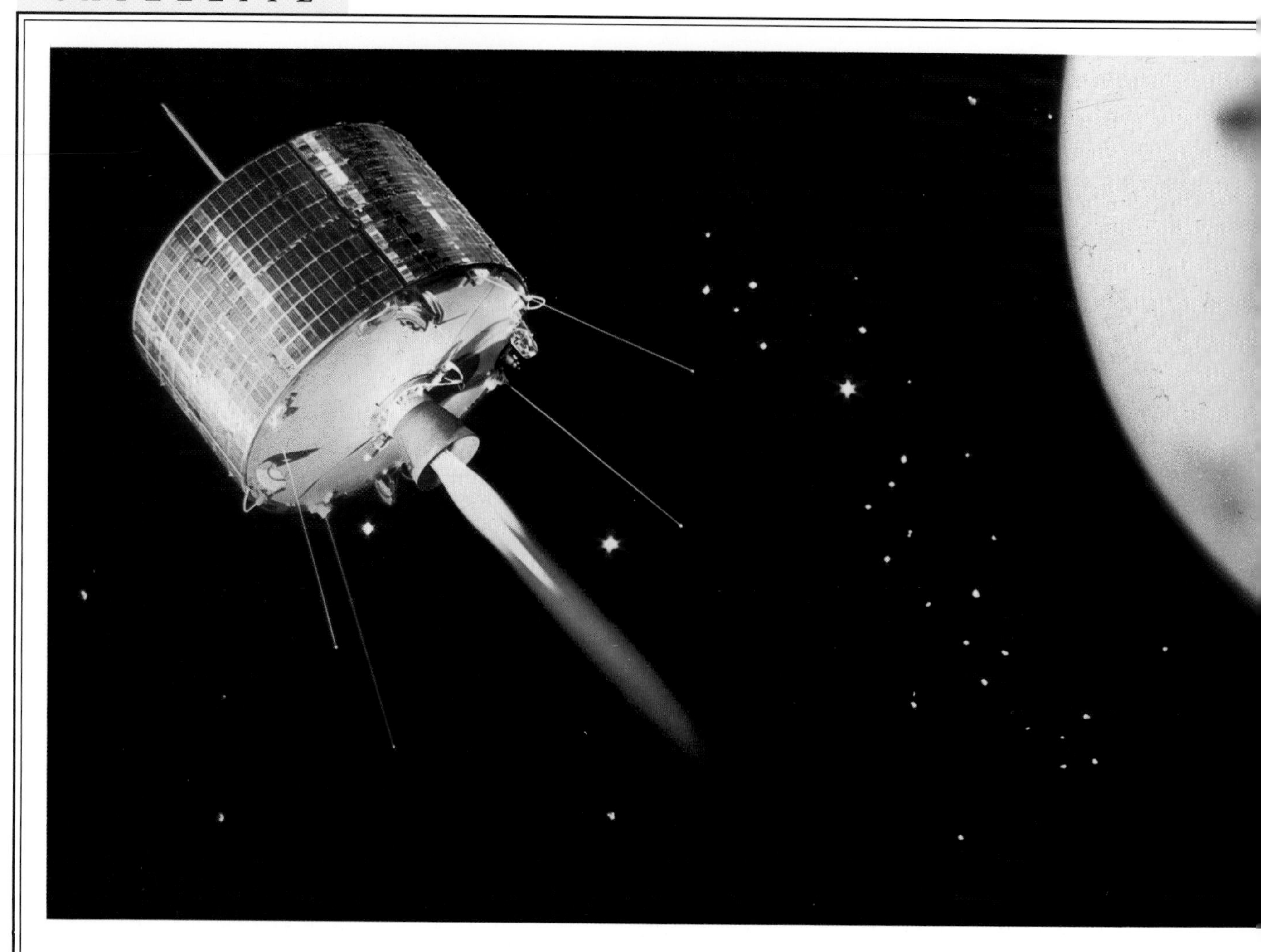

Artificial satellites follow various types of orbits. Satellites in a polar orbit cross over the North and South poles each time they journey around the earth. Satellites in a synchronous orbit revolve around the earth at the same speed that the earth rotates. Thus, they remain in orbit above a specific region of the earth.

Components and uses of artificial satellites All artificial satellites have several major components. They all have a power supply. For example, many satellites use solar energy, which is collected by solar panels mounted on the surface of the satellite (see SOLAR CELL; SOLAR ENERGY). Satellites also have scientific instruments to collect information. They have equipment to transmit information back to Earth. They have extra rockets that can be fired to correct their position when necessary. They have computers, either on board or on Earth, that control many of the functions of the satellite, such as collecting information.

SYNCOM

Syncom—short for *synchronous communications satellite*—is used to carry radio signals between continents. Orbiting about 22,000 mi. [35,200 km] above the earth, it completes one orbit every twenty-four hours, which is the same amount of time it takes the earth to rotate once on its axis. As a result, the satellite appears to remain stationary over the same point on the earth.

Artificial satellites serve five basic purposes: communication; weather forecasting; navigation plotting; military surveillance; and scientific observation of the earth, atmosphere, and space.

Communications satellites help transmit radio, television, and telephone signals from different parts of the earth. The first communications satellites launched were called passive satellites. This was because they acted much like mirrors, reflecting signals from one part of the earth to another. Today's satellites are called active satellites. These satellites not only relay signals from one part of the earth to another, they also amplify (strengthen) the signals. By amplifying the signals, satellites improve the quality of transmission.

Weather satellites transmit photographic images of the earth's atmosphere. These images are used by meteorologists to map weather patterns and to detect dangerous storms. Weather satellites serve as an early warning system for storms and help meteorologists understand how weather patterns develop (see METEOROLOGY). Images from weather satellites are also useful in studying pollution.

Navigation satellites help ships and aircraft determine their exact location, no matter what the weather or the time of day. The U.S. Global Positioning System consists of twenty-four satellites that enable users in the U.S. military to find their position to within 5 ft. [1.5 m]. Others can use the system to obtain their position accurate to within 330 ft. [100 m]. Each satellite sends out a continuous radio signal. To fix position, a user needs to be within range of four satellites. The user's receiver can calculate the position from the signals received from each satellite. Another satellite navigation system, called Transit, makes use of twelve satellites. It can locate users to within 330 ft. [100 m] (see NAVIGATION).

Military satellites are used to listen to foreign radio and telephone conversations. Satellites can also be used to transmit detailed photographic images of foreign territory. These images are useful in monitoring foreign troops and in selecting targets to attack.

Scientific satellites make it possible for scientists to observe and study many different phenomena. IRAS (Infrared Astronomical Satellite), which was launched in 1983, carried out a complete infrared survey of the skies. Solar Max, launched in 1980, observed solar flares. The Hipparcos satellite, launched in 1989, measured the positions of many stars with accuracy not achieved before. In 1992, the COBE (Cosmic Background Explorer) satellite detected radiation that marked the first stage in the formation of the universe after the big bang (see BIG BANG THEORY). The Hubble Space Telescope, launched in 1990, performs much better than any ground-based telescope because it is above the atmosphere.

Satellites equipped with instruments such as radar and infrared detectors take inventory of land and sea resources (see INFRARED RAY; RADAR). Forests, lakes, and rivers can be surveyed by such satellites. Data from the satellites make it possible, for example, to estimate the size of rain forests and calculate how quickly they are being cut down. These satellites also enable mapmakers to make more accurate maps of the earth (see MAP AND MAPPING).

Many satellites are launched to test uses for future satellites. These tests may lead to improvements in the design and reliability of control systems, power supplies, and communications systems. The space shuttle developed by the United States can place satellites in orbit. It can later take astronauts back to the satellites to repair or modify them while they are in orbit.

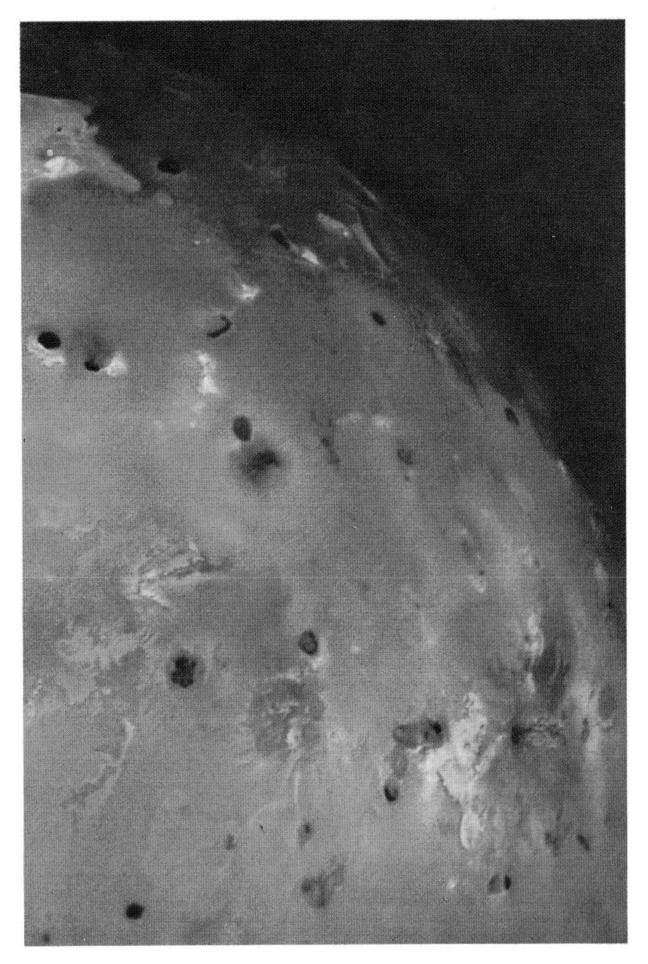

NATURAL SATELLITE

Io is the innermost natural satellite—or moon—of the planet Jupiter. This close-up picture was taken by the *Voyager 1* spacecraft and reveals features as small as about 6 mi. [10 km] across.

SATURN

Saturn, the second largest planet in our solar system, is sixth in order from the sun (see PLANET; SOLAR SYSTEM). Saturn is famous for its magnificent system of rings that orbit the planet's equator.

The diameter of Saturn is about 74,600 mi. [120,031 km] through the equator. The diameter through Saturn's poles is about 67,200 mi. [108,125 km]. The average distance of Saturn from the sun is about 886 million mi. [1,425 million km]. It takes the planet 29.46 years to make one complete trip around the sun. Saturn makes a complete spin on its axis (an imaginary line running through the planet from pole to pole) every 10 hours, 39 minutes. Its axis is tilted about 27°.

Saturn is a yellowish color with darker bands that run parallel to the equator. The polar regions appear slightly greenish.

Because it consists mainly of hydrogen, Saturn is the least dense of the planets (see DENSITY). The surface of Saturn is believed to be covered with liquid hydrogen. The pressures in the interior of the planet probably compress the hydrogen into a solid form. At the center of the planet, heavier elements may have formed a solid core. The temperature at the center of the planet is estimated at 27,000°F [15,000°C].

Saturn's thick, opaque atmosphere consists mostly of hydrogen and helium. Temperatures of about -285°F [-176°C] have been measured at the top of its clouds. The surface temperature of Saturn is estimated to be only -290°F [-179°C], due to Saturn's great distance from the sun. Wind speeds reach 1,060 m.p.h. [1,700 kph] near the equator.

Evidence of Saturn's rings was first seen, with the aid of a telescope, by the Italian scientist Galileo (see GALILEO; TELESCOPE). Later, astronomers were able to distinguish seven rings. They labeled these rings D, C, B, A, F, G, and E, with D closest to the planet and E farthest away. In 1980, astronomers discovered that the rings are actually made up of countless ringlets. Rings B and A are visible from Earth with the aid of a telescope. The other rings were seen with space telescopes. The rings vary in width; for example, B is more than 15,000 mi. [25,000 km] wide, while A is about 9,000 mi. [15,000 km] wide. None of the rings is more than 1.2 mi. [2 km] thick, and at their thinnest, they are only about 300 ft. [100 m]. The rings probably consist of ice, dust, and frozen gases.

Saturn has twenty-three moons. The largest, Titan, is 3,090 mi. [5,150 km] in diameter. Thus, Titan is about the same size as the planet Mercury. It is the only known moon in the solar system that has a measurable atmosphere. The thick orange haze of Titan's atmosphere consists mostly of nitrogen. Saturn's six smallest moons, discovered by the *Voyager* space probes, are each only about 12 mi. [20 km] across.

See also SPACE EXPLORATION.

SATURN'S STRUCTURE

Saturn probably has a small iron-silicate core, surrounded by liquid metallic hydrogen. Most of the planet consists of liquid molecular hydrogen, with a thick atmosphere of hydrogen and helium.

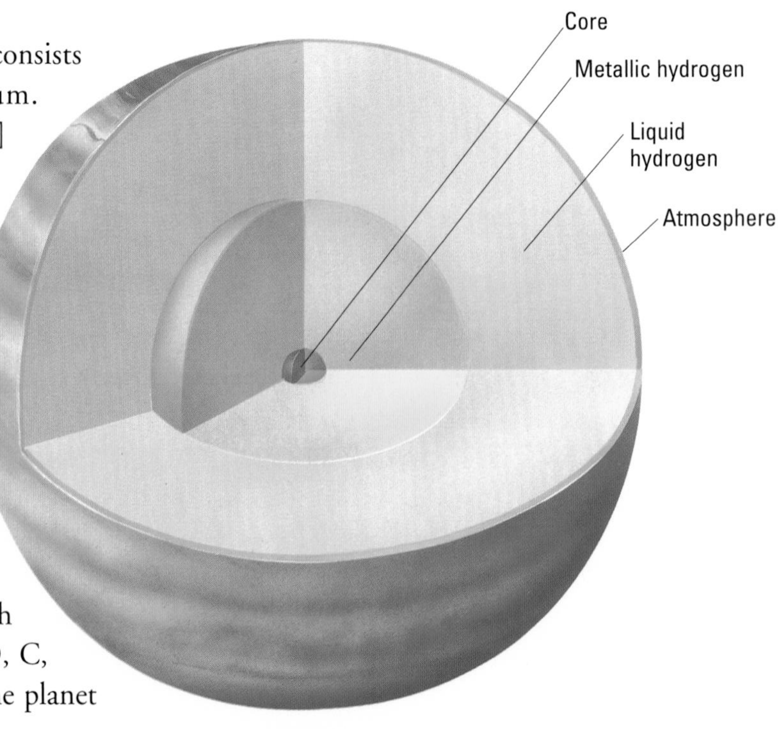

SATURN'S RINGS

Saturn is noted for the rings that orbit the planet's equator (above). In closeup (left), the rings are seen to consist of countless ringlets, probably made up of ice, dust, and various frozen gases.

SAWFISH
The sawfish is a relative of the shark. Sawfish use their saw-edged snouts for digging up shellfish and other invertebrates that they eat.

SAWFISH A sawfish is a saltwater fish in the family Pristidae. It is a cartilaginous fish related to the sharks (see FISH; SHARK). The sawfish gets its name from its long, flattened snout, which looks like a saw. The edges of the snout have sharp teeth. The snout is used by the fish to stir up the ocean bottom to find the mollusks and other invertebrates that it eats (see INVERTEBRATE; MOLLUSCA). It is also used to attack fish, disabling them so they can be eaten. There are several species of sawfish, but only two—the smalltooth sawfish and the largetooth sawfish—are found off North America. Some sawfish reach 20 ft. [6 m] in length and weigh over 1 ton [0.9 metric ton].

SAWFLY Sawflies are insects that, like ants, bees, and wasps, belong to the order Hymenoptera (see INSECT). The name *sawfly* refers to the sawlike ovipositor that most female sawflies have. The ovipositor is a special egg-laying tube. The female uses the ovipositor to cut slits in leaves and to lay eggs in these slits. Some sawflies have a drill-like ovipositor for laying eggs in woody twigs and stems.

Sawfly eggs hatch into larvae (plural of *larva*) (see LARVA). Most larvae feed on the leaves of trees and shrubs. Other larvae bore into stems and feed on sap (see SAP). In late fall, the larva forms a cocoon and spends the winter as a pupa (see COCOON; PUPA). In spring, the pupa becomes an adult (see METAMORPHOSIS). The adults usually feed on nectar, a sweet liquid found in many flowers. Some species, however, eat pollen and small insects (see POLLEN).

One of the most common sawflies is the pear "slug." It is found throughout the world and causes great damage to the leaves of many fruit trees.

SAXIFRAGE FAMILY The saxifrage (săk′sə frĭj) family includes about 580 species of perennial herbaceous plants (see HERBACEOUS PLANT; PERENNIAL PLANT). These plants are usually found in cold and temperate areas of the Northern Hemisphere. Most members of the saxifrage family grow on or between rocks. The leaves are often tightly packed into circular clusters. The plants are very popular in rock gardens.

The flowers grow in clusters. Each flower usually has five sepals, five colorful petals, one or two whorls of five stamens, and two pistils (see FLOWER). The fruit is a capsule that contains many seeds.
See also FRUIT.

SAXIFRAGE FAMILY
Unlike most saxifrages, which grow low on the ground, the meadow saxifrage (above) has flowers on long stems that grow taller than the surrounding grass.

SCALE Most maps are drawn to scale. This means that a given distance on the map represents a certain, larger distance on the earth's surface. Scale is sometimes shown in the legend, or key, of the map as a straight line divided into miles or kilometers. This is called a graphic scale.

Sometimes, the scale is written in words and figures, such as 1 inch = 3 miles. Other scales are written as proportions, such as 1: 100,000. This means that 1 unit of measurement on the map represents 100,000 units on the ground. For example, if the distance between two points on a map drawn at this scale is 3.5 in. [8.7 cm], the actual distance between the places represented is 5.4 mi. [8.7 km].

Mapmakers distinguish between small-scale maps, which show large areas, and large-scale maps, which show relatively small areas. Small-scale maps show much less detail than large-scale maps.
See also MAP AND MAPPING.

SCALE INSECT Scale insects are small insects that belong to order Homoptera. Like the other members of this order, scale insects have a sharp, beaklike structure called a proboscis, which they use to pierce plants and suck out their juices. After hatching, a young scale insect lands on a leaf or other plant part and jabs its proboscis into the plant. The plant then becomes its permanent home. Once attached, the scale insect may molt into a nonmoving, legless form (see MOLTING).

Female scale insects are wingless and have small legs and antennae (see ANTENNAE). A female secretes a waxy liquid that hardens into a tough flap called a scale. She then lives and lays eggs underneath this covering. Some species do not lay eggs but give birth to living young. Males are very small and usually have one pair of delicate wings. Some males are wingless. The males have no mouth parts. Thus, they do not eat. In some species, males are rare, and the females lay eggs that develop by parthenogenesis (see PARTHENOGENESIS).

The Indian lac insect produces a scale that is used in making shellac (see SHELLAC). Many scale insects are serious pests and may cover completely some part—roots, stems, or leaves—of a plant. The California citrus industry was almost destroyed by scale insects that were introduced from Australia in the 1860s.

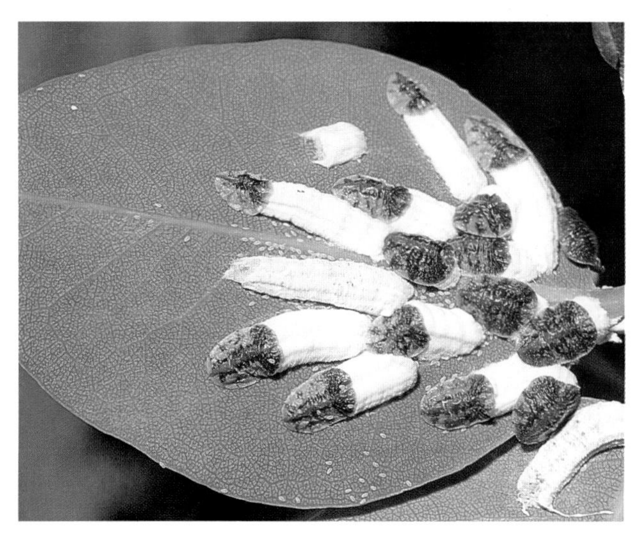

SCALE INSECT
Female scale insects lay masses of white eggs and can almost completely cover the leaves of plants.

SCALLOP (skŏl′əp) The scallop is a bivalve (two-shelled) mollusk closely related to the oyster (see BIVALVE; MOLLUSCA; OYSTER). There are more than four hundred species of scallops. The animals have a worldwide distribution and range from shallow water to ocean depths of 2,000 ft. [600 m].

The scallop's shells, or valves, are usually fan-shaped and sometimes ribbed. One valve is flat and the other is saucer-shaped. At the hinge, where the ligament (tough fibrous tissue) connects the two

SCALLOP
The queen scallop has a row of eyes around the edge of each of its shells.

valves, there are two winglike projections. The inside of the shell is lined with a membrane called a mantle (see MEMBRANE). Each edge of this mantle is folded and fringed with slender growths called tentacles and a row of eyes.

Scallops are quite active. They swim by rapidly opening and closing their valves. When the valves close, the water between the valves is forced out in small jets through openings near the hinge. This pushes the creature forward in a zigzag pattern.

Several species of scallops are found along the Atlantic coast of North America. The most important of these is the common scallop. Common scallops may be found in bays and inlets from Nova Scotia to the Gulf of Mexico. The deep-sea scallop may grow to 8 in. [20 cm] in width. It is found especially along the coasts of Maine and Nova Scotia.

Scallops are a popular and commercially important food item. The large muscle that closes the animal's valves is the part of the scallop that is eaten.

SCANNING TUNNELING MICROSCOPE A scanning tunneling microscope is a very sensitive type of microscope used to probe the smallest details of surfaces (see MICROSCOPE). It can be used to view individual atoms (see ATOM). The probe of a typical scanning tunneling microscope is about the size of a thumb, although the electronics and display components are considerably larger. In the microscope, a metal tip that narrows to a single atom at its point is positioned so close to a surface that electrons from the atoms at the top of the surface jump, or "tunnel," from the surface onto the tip. When the electrons move, they form an electric current. The size of the current depends on the distance between the tip and the surface. As the tip is scanned (moved) across the surface, it is raised or lowered to keep the electric current the same. The up-and-down movement of the tip is converted into a map of the surface. Bumps in the map show the positions of atoms.

Scanning tunneling microscopes now have many interesting uses. Because the scanning probe tips can also be used to pick up atoms, move them, and place them in another position with great precision, miniature scanning tunneling microscopes could be used to move atoms into piles to create a new way of storing data in computers. Scientists are also using a modified form of a scanning tunneling microscope to study the surface of teeth to find out why some people's teeth are very sensitive to hot and cold and to find a way to prevent this.

SCARAB (skăr'əb) The scarab family (Scarabaeidae) includes about 20,000 species of beetles that are found throughout the world (see BEETLE). These insects belong to the order Coleoptera. One of the world's largest insects, the African goliath beetle, is a member of the scarab family. It sometimes reaches a length of more than 4 in. [10 cm]. The Japanese beetle is another member of the scarab family. This insect was accidentally introduced into the United States in 1916. Since then, it has caused widespread damage to plants throughout North America. The adult Japanese beetle eats leaves, often destroying a plant in the process. Each female beetle lays hundreds of eggs, which hatch into larvae (plural of *larva*) near the end of the summer (see LARVA). These larvae feed on roots and spend the winter underground. They emerge as adults in the spring, when they begin the cycle of plant destruction once again.

Dung beetles, or tumblebugs, are scarabs that

SCARAB

There are about twenty thousand different kinds of scarab beetles found worldwide. Some species feed on plants and can cause damage to lawns and food crops. The scarab pictured is commonly found in Africa.

belong to subfamily Scarabaeinae (see DUNG BEETLE). These beetles are so named because they roll animal dung into balls and then bury it. Eggs are laid in these balls. When the eggs hatch, the larvae feed on the dung until they turn into pupae (see METAMORPHOSIS; PUPA). One species of dung beetles was considered sacred by the ancient Egyptians. The Egyptians believed that the beetle represented the sun and that the short spines on the beetle's thorax represented the sun's rays (see THORAX). They also believed that the dung ball represented the earth. Many other scarabs feed on dung without burying it. They are important scavengers (see SCAVENGER).
See also INSECT.

SCARLET FEVER Scarlet fever (also called *scarlatina*) is an infectious disease that affects mainly children (see DISEASE; INFECTION). It is named for the bright red skin rash that develops when a person has the disease. Scarlet fever is caused by one of a group of bacteria called group A *Streptococcus.* These bacteria may also cause tonsilitis or strep throat (see STREP THROAT; TONSIL). Some people infected with this type of bacterium (singular of *bacteria*) may get only a sore throat. However, these people can spread the bacteria, which can then cause scarlet fever in others.

Scarlet fever develops rapidly. Symptoms include high fever, rapid pulse, headache, muscle pain, and nausea. The rash, consisting of red spots, appears shortly after the onset of the disease. It disappears after several days. Then the skin starts to peel. Toxins (poisons) given off by the bacteria cause the rash and the peeling. The toxins may affect other organs, sometimes causing damage to the heart and kidneys. A few patients become susceptible to other infections, such as pneumonia and meningitis, because their body is weakened from the scarlet fever. Scarlet fever is most serious in children less than one year old. As children grow older, they develop more resistance to the disease (see IMMUNITY).

To keep the disease from spreading, patients are usually kept apart from other persons. Doctors often give the antibiotic penicillin, which is very effective against the bacteria (see ANTIBIOTIC; PENICILLIN). Sometimes, doctors inject gamma globulin, a medicine prepared from human serum (see SERUM). Gamma globulin helps the person recover from the infection.

SCARP A scarp is a steep inland slope that rises sharply from level land. It is formed when layers of hard rock are tilted upward by movements of the earth's surface.

Some fault scarps have been created by series of earthquakes (see EARTHQUAKE; FAULT). For example, during an earthquake in Assam, India, in 1897, the land on one side of the fault moved upward relative to the land on the other side, creating a scarp that is 36 ft. [12 m] high.

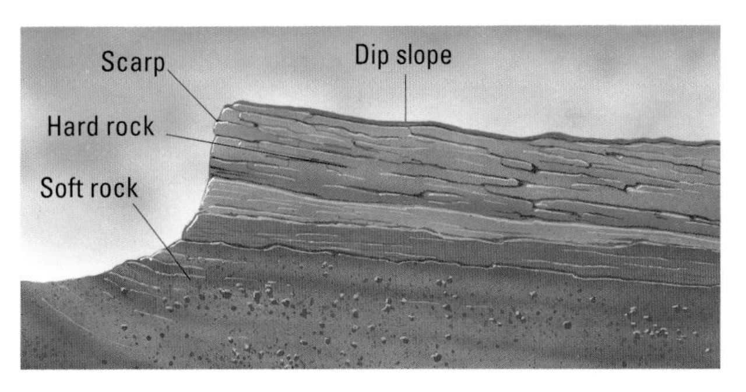

SCARP
A scarp is a steep, inland slope that rises sharply from level land. It is formed when layers of rock are tilted by movements of the earth's surface. The hard rock capping the tilted layers resists erosion. The gentle slope leading to a scarp is called the dip slope.

SCATTERING Scattering is the deflection of light or other radiation that occurs when the radiation hits particles of matter (see RADIATION). When a ray of sunlight passes through misty, smoky, or dusty air, we can see it because of the scattering effect of the particles in the air. Light is scattered in all directions, and some of the deflected light reaches our eyes. Some of the light energy is absorbed whenever a ray of light bounces off a surface, even the surface of the tiniest particle. Every time scattered light hits a particle, more energy is absorbed. Thick smoke, with its billions of tiny particles that scatter and absorb light energy, quickly absorbs rays of light that pass into it. This effect explains, in part, why smoke is difficult to see through.

The British scientist Lord Rayleigh demonstrated

the rule that governs the scattering of light. He showed that light of short wavelengths (at the violet end of the spectrum) is scattered much more than long wavelengths of light (at the red end of the spectrum) (see LIGHT; SPECTRUM; WAVELENGTH). This kind of scattering is called Rayleigh scattering.

Rayleigh scattering explains why the sky appears blue. Atoms and molecules of gases in the atmosphere scatter all wavelengths of the sun's light. However, the shorter wavelengths of light, including the blue light, are scattered more than the longer wavelengths of light. Thus, more blue light reaches our eyes when we look at the sky, and so the sky appears blue. If the earth had no atmosphere, there would be no scattering of light. Then, the sky would appear black, as it does to astronauts outside the earth's atmosphere.

Knowledge of the rules of scattering has made it possible to design efficient automobile lights for use in fog. Blue light in the beam from a headlight is quickly scattered and lost in fog. It does not penetrate very far. On the other hand, it is difficult to produce a really bright red light (except by means of a laser) that illuminates objects clearly. Fog lights use the next best wavelengths, with bright orange or yellow colors, to penetrate fog.

PROJECT 41

SCAVENGER A scavenger, or scavenging animal, is one that feeds on dead, decaying matter. The name is used especially for those animals that eat the remains of other animals' prey. Vultures are important scavengers on the African plains, where they quickly reduce the carcasses (dead bodies) of antelopes and other animals to piles of bones (see VULTURE). Scavengers also include a wide range of beetles and other insects that feed on dead leaves and wood (see DUNG BEETLE). Some beetles even chew through the bones and skin left behind by carnivores and untouched by other scavenging animals.

Scavengers play an important role in recycling organic (carbon-containing) materials (see CARBON CYCLE; NITROGEN CYCLE). Without scavengers (and decomposers such as bacteria and fungi), we would soon be buried in dead bodies, animal dung, and other waste material.

SCAVENGER

Termites are typical scavengers. Here they are collecting dead leaves, which they will use as a "compost" on which to grow mushrooms inside the termite nest.

PROJECT 65

SCHEELE, CARL WILHELM (1742–1786) (shā′ lə, kärl wĭl′ hĕlm) Carl Scheele was a Swedish chemist who made many discoveries about elements and compounds (see COMPOUND; ELEMENT). Scheele was born at Stralsund, Pomerania, which is now part of Germany. He worked for a pharmacist and taught himself chemistry.

Scheele was a brilliant researcher. He was among the first people to synthesize (make by combining parts) many acids, including oxalic acid, citric acid, tartaric acid, and lactic acid. He also discovered methods for making hydrogen sulfide, hydrogen fluoride, and hydrogen cyanide. He discovered many elements, including chlorine, manganese, barium, molybdenum, tungsten, nitrogen, and oxygen. Scheele, however, is rarely given credit for these discoveries. This is because other chemists were doing the same kind of work as Scheele and often published their results before Scheele published his.

Scheele studied a substance made from copper and arsenic, which is called Scheele's green. Scheelite, a mineral ore of tungsten, is also named for him (see ORE).

SCHIST (shĭst) Schist is a type of metamorphic rock in which the minerals are arranged so that the rock splits into layers (see METAMORPHIC ROCK; MINERAL). This characteristic is known as schistose cleavage.

Schists are classified according to the minerals they contain. For example, mica schist contains layers of shiny mica, while talc schist is rich in talc (see MICA; TALC). Some schists are made into flagstones to be used for fireplaces.

SCHIST
Schist (above) is a type of metamorphic rock formed by heat and pressure beneath the earth's surface. The minerals in schist are arranged so that the rock easily splits into layers.

SCHISTOSOMIASIS (shĭs′tō sə mī′ə sĭs) Schistosomiasis is a parasitic disease found only in warm climates (see DISEASE; PARASITE). The parasitic worm that causes the disease is called a schistosome. Schistosomes are found in South America, some Caribbean islands, Africa, the Middle East, China, and the Philippines. In the past, the disease was called bilharzia.

The larva, or immature form, of the schistosome lives in water (see LARVA). It attaches itself to the skin of a human being and burrows into the skin. Once inside the body, the schistosome larva travels to large veins, where it can cause an inflammatory reaction that injures body tissues (see INFLAMMATION). Schistosomiasis is difficult to treat, though there are drugs that kill the parasites and are safe and effective. Untreated, the disease can be fatal. Scientists are trying to control the disease by killing the worm larvae (plural of *larva*) in infected water and improving sanitation near water sources.

SCHRÖDINGER, ERWIN (1887–1961) (shrō′ dĭng ər, ĕr′ vĭn) Erwin Schrödinger was an Austrian physicist who developed a mathematical explanation for the way electrons and other subatomic particles behave (see ATOM; ELECTRON). This equation, which is now known as the Schrödinger equation, was important in the development of the quantum theory (see QUANTUM THEORY). In 1933, Schrödinger shared the Nobel Prize for physics with the English physicist Paul Dirac. Schrödinger was born in Vienna; taught in Zurich, Switzerland, and Berlin, Germany; and wrote several books, including books about philosophy and the history of science.
See also PARTICLE PHYSICS.

SCHWANN, THEODOR (1810–1882) (shwän, tā′ ō dôr′) Theodor Schwann was a German doctor and biologist who made significant discoveries about the importance of the cell (see CELL). He was born in Neuss. He became professor of anatomy at Louvain and later at Liege, both in Belgium.

Schwann studied many different life processes. He discovered the enzyme pepsin, which digests protein (see ENZYME; PROTEIN). He also studied the way muscles work. In 1838, he made the observation that yeast is a kind of single-cell organism that feeds on sugar. However, Schwann is most famous for developing the cell theory of living things in conjunction with Matthias Schleiden. The cell theory, as proposed by Schwann and Schleiden, states that all living things are made of cells. Schleiden had already begun to formulate this theory, but Schwann continued to work out many more details. He recognized that plant and animal cells were similar in many ways. He saw that an egg is a single cell containing yolk and that the growth of an egg is a multiplication of cells. He also saw that different tissues are made of different types of cells (see TISSUE). The cells that make up the myelin sheaths that cover some nerve cells are called Schwann cells after him.
See also NERVE CELL.

SCIENCE

Science is the term for the broad field of human knowledge concerned with facts that are explained logically by rules, patterns, or principles. Scientists discover these facts and test their explanations by the scientific method, an orderly procedure for asking questions, generating answers, and solving problems. Any subject that people can study by using the scientific method is called a science.

The sciences include mathematics and logic; the physical sciences, such as physics and chemistry; the biological sciences, such as zoology and botany; and the social sciences, such as anthropology and sociology.

AREAS OF SCIENCE

Science is made up of many different areas of study. There is overlap among many of the areas. In addition, these areas can be broken down into smaller areas, or subdisciplines.

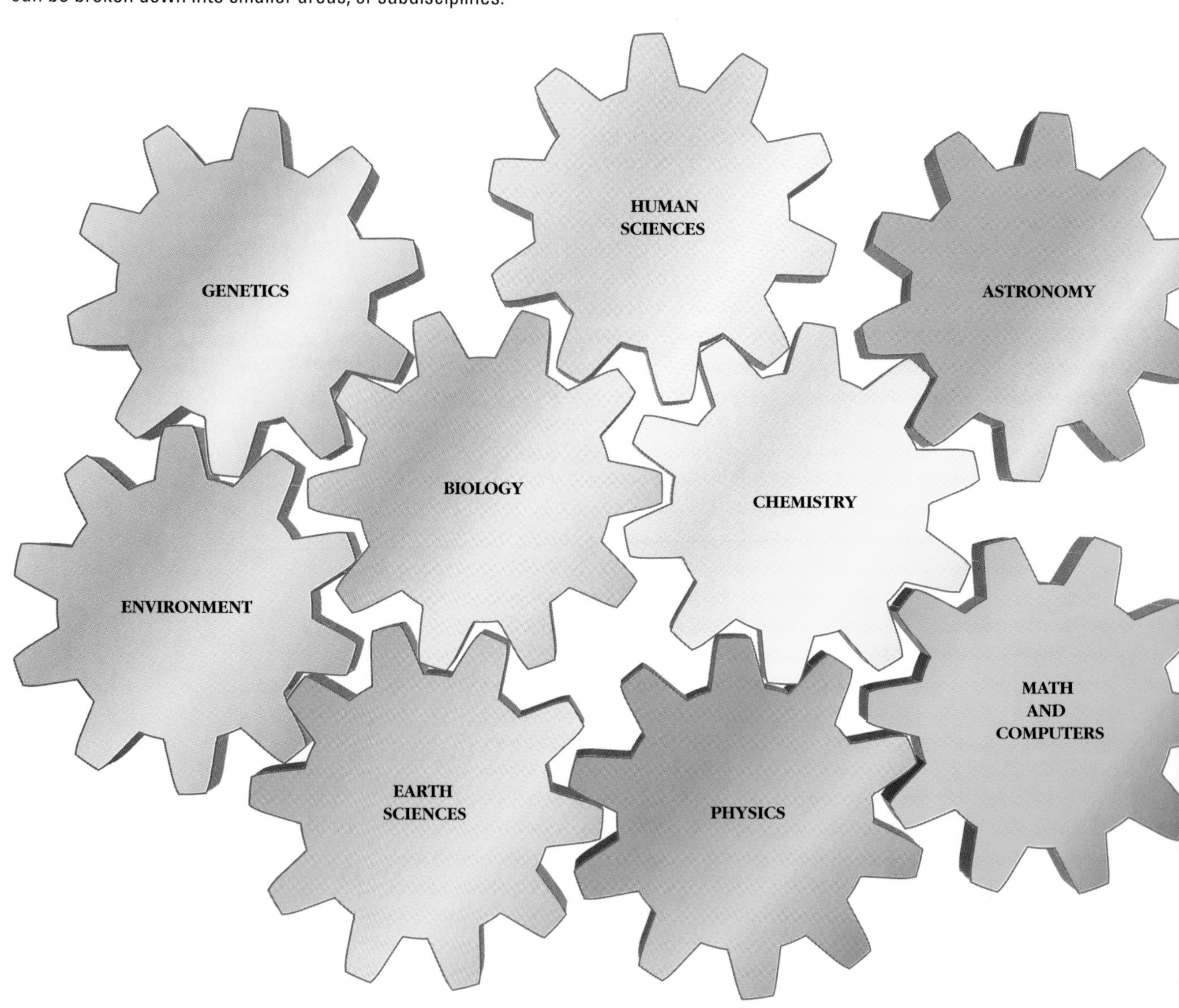

Scientific study can be divided into pure science and applied science. Pure science summarizes and explains the facts and principles discovered about the universe and its inhabitants. Applied science uses these scientific facts and principles to make things that are useful to people.

Science often involves classifying things—for example, determining to what species a plant or animal belongs. Scientists are also concerned with causes and effects and being able to measure them.

Scientists require exact language to describe the things and events they are studying. Many times, the discoveries that scientists make about events are new. They often have to create words to explain their discoveries. The words may be derived from

Latin or Greek. Many plant and animal names are derived from these languages. In other cases, the words are entirely new, such as *quark* and *laser*.

Scientific method In doing their work, scientists use what is called the scientific method. The scientific method involves several steps: identifying the problem; gathering all the known information: and forming a hypothesis, or assumption. The hypothesis offers a possible explanation for an event that has been observed. To test the hypothesis, the scientist designs and performs experiments, where possible under controlled conditions that allow the event to be affected by only one thing (variable) at a time. He or she makes careful observations during the experiments. The scientist then draws a conclusion, deciding whether the experiment supports the hypothesis. Before the hypothesis is accepted, other scientists have to perform the experiment and get the same results. Sometimes, a hypothesis is soon found to be untrue. A new hypothesis then has to be developed. Other times, a hypothesis is believed to be true for many years before it is proved wrong. Sometimes, there is no way to test a hypothesis.

For example, Newton's laws of motion were accepted for many years (see DYNAMICS; NEWTON, SIR ISAAC). However, as more observations of different events were made, it was found that Newton's laws did not hold for motion at speeds close to the speed of light. In the early 1900s, Albert Einstein published his theories of relativity, which introduced a new way of looking at motion. (A theory, like a hypothesis, is a possible explanation, but one that has been widely tested and is therefore more likely to be true) (see EINSTEIN, ALBERT; RELATIVITY). Einstein's theories led to many conclusions that were regarded at that time as strange and unbelievable. However, numerous observations and experiments have since upheld the predictions of Einstein's theories. These theories more accurately explain motion at speeds close to the speed of light. They also show that at much slower speeds, Newton's laws accurately explain motion. In this way, Einstein's theory encompassed Newton's laws and went on to explain other events that Newton had not studied. Thus, Einstein's modification of Newton's laws of motion has helped scientists discover more about the universe.

Science today In the past four hundred years, scientists have made many advances in many fields. However, scientific discovery is an ongoing

CHEMISTRY

Chemistry is a branch of science that concentrates on making or analyzing substances. Here a chemist is setting up equipment to make a new type of drug.

MODERN SCIENCE

Science has progressed greatly during the past four hundred years. Computers have revolutionized recent scientific development. The computer allows scientists to produce visual models of complex chemicals.

process, and scientists will always be making new discoveries that will give us a better understanding of our universe.

In physics, scientists are using particle accelerators to learn more about the structure of the atom and of subatomic particles (see ACCELERATORS, PARTICLE; ATOM; PARTICLE PHYSICS). Through this work, they are now generating different theories about the nature of matter and about the fundamental building blocks of the universe.

Astronomers are always discovering new stars and new galaxies (groups of stars). By observing how stars change over long periods of time and how galaxies are arranged, they hope to find out more about how our solar system and our planet originated (see ASTRONOMY).

Medical scientists are studying specific diseases to learn their causes and how they can be prevented. They are testing new medicines that can help cure many kinds of disease (see DISEASE; MEDICINE).

In biology and botany, scientists are studying details of the different processes that plant and animal cells undergo. They are studying how the genes control various cell processes (see CELL; GENETICS). Biochemists are trying to recreate conditions similar to those that existed when the earth was young. In this way, they hope to learn more about how life originated.

History of science The history of science can be traced back to prehistoric times. Numerical records carved in stone show that ancient peoples had a knowledge of counting. Clay tablets from Mesopotamia demonstrate knowledge of astronomy, medicine, chemistry, and mathematics. The ancient Babylonians developed algebra and a system of measurement based on the number 60. Egyptian documents from the same period contain information on medicine and solid geometry.

However, early scientific knowledge was poorly organized. The ancient Greeks first began to systematize science. In the fourth century B.C., the philosopher Plato's Academy in Athens emphasized deductive reasoning and mathematical representation. Aristotle's Lyceum (school) taught inductive reasoning and qualitative description (see ARISTOTLE). (In deductive reasoning, a person reasons from general laws to particular cases; in inductive reasoning, a person reasons from particular cases to general laws. In qualitative description, a person describes something as opposed to measuring it.) The interplay between these two approaches has led to most advances in science.

During the fourth century B.C., an accurate measurement of the earth, a theory of a sun-centered planetary system, the beginnings of botany, and anatomical/physiological studies based on dissection were developed. In this same period, the so-called Hellenistic Age, Archimedes laid the foundations of mechanics and hydrostatics, and the astronomer Hipparchus developed trigonometry (see ARCHIMEDES; HIPPARCHUS). Some great advances were also made in the second century A.D., with Ptolemy's observations in astronomy and the medical writings of Galen, a physician and philosopher (see GALEN; PTOLEMY).

During the Middle Ages, the Chinese and Indian cultures were the sources of major scientific advances. The Chinese invented the mariner's compass and devices to predict and detect earthquakes. In India, the Arabic numerals in use today were developed. A more modern form of trigonometry also came from India. Much of the Indian knowledge was transmitted to Europe by the Arabs in the twelfth century.

Science in sixteenth-century Europe experienced a revival after centuries of disruption. Copernicus published his famous work on the solar system (see COPERNICUS). Vesalius published his book on the human body that corrected and modernized Galen's works and led to the discovery of the circulation of blood. The modern period in algebra began in the middle of the century.

What are considered modern scientific methods and results began to appear in the seventeenth century, when Galileo made systematic verification through planned experiments an important part of science. Galileo used the newly developed telescope, microscope, and thermometer in his studies (see GALILEO). The barometer, pendulum clock, and exhaust pump also were invented. Sir Isaac Newton and Gottfried Wilhelm Leibniz developed a new branch of mathematics at the same time. This branch, called calculus, became the basis of modern physics.

The nineteenth century saw such developments as the atomic theory of matter, the theory of electromagnetism, and the law of conservation of energy. Darwin's theory of evolution was also developed during this period (see DARWIN, CHARLES; EVOLUTION).

The twentieth century has seen such great advances as modern atomic theory, new surgical and medical techniques, the development of electronics and computers, and space travel.

See also CHEMISTRY; PHYSICS.

SCLERENCHYMA (sklə rĕng′kə mə) Sclerenchyma is a strong, hard, nonliving tissue found in plants. It is made up of cells that have lost their protoplasm (see PROTOPLASM). The cell walls are thickened with large amounts of cellulose and usually lignin as well (see CELLULOSE; LIGNIN). Sclerenchyma often forms fibers in the cortex, phloem, and xylem of woody roots and stems (see CORTEX; PHLOEM; XYLEM). This adds strength, support, and protection to the stems. Sclerenchyma is also found in layers in the woody shells of nuts and in seed coats. Single sclerenchyma cells are sometimes called stone cells. They give pears a gritty or sandy texture.

SCORPION The scorpion is a small animal that, along with spiders and ticks, is a type of arachnid (see ARACHNID). The stinger, found at the end of the body, is one unique feature of the scorpion. Scorpions are found in warmer parts of the world. About twenty different kinds of scorpions live in the United States.

Scorpions are usually black or yellowish, ranging from 0.5 to 7 in. [1.3 to 17.5 cm] in length. The body of the scorpion has two parts. The cephalothorax, which is the thick, forward part, consists of the head and chest. Behind the cephalothorax is the abdomen, which tapers to form a "tail" (see ABDOMEN; THORAX). This tail has a stinger at the tip. Two glands at the base of the tail give out a poison that flows from two openings (see GLAND).

The scorpion has six pairs of appendages. The first pair, called chelicerae, are used to tear apart prey. The second pair, called pedipalps, are large and have strong clawlike pincers. These are held horizontally in front and are used as feelers and for grasping prey. The last four pairs, each equipped with two small claws, are walking legs.

Scorpions are nocturnal (active at night). They feed chiefly on insects and spiders. Female scorpions bear their young alive.

Most people fear the scorpion because of its sting. At least two general types of scorpions exist. One type of scorpion has a sting that causes some pain but is not fatal. The other type of scorpion injects a dangerous nerve poison when it stings. The sting of this type of scorpion can cause death. However, most scorpions prefer to retreat rather than fight. They do not usually sting human beings.

SCORPION FLY Scorpion flies include about three hundred species of insects, most of which belong to the family Panorpidae. The male scorpion fly holds the tip of its tail over its abdomen, much the way that the scorpion holds its stinger.

SCORPION
Scorpions, such as the one shown right, are found mainly in warmer parts of the world. They have a stinger at the end of their upwardly curved tail. The sting of a few species can be fatal, but most are no more harmful than the sting of a bee or a wasp.

However, the scorpion fly does not sting and is harmless. Scorpion flies are usually about 0.5 to 1 in. [1.2 to 2.5 cm] long. Although most scorpion flies have two pairs of spotted wings, some are wingless. Scorpion flies have long antennae and long, thin legs (see ANTENNAE). They usually live in cool, moist, wooded areas.

Most scorpion flies are omnivorous, eating both plant and animal material. Some hang upside down from leaves, holding on with their front legs. These hanging flies use their long hind legs to capture other flying insects.

See also INSECT.

SCREW A screw is a cylindrical or tapering piece of metal or other strong material with a helical groove (like a spiral staircase) cut into it. Each turn of the screw moves it backward or forward. The screw moves forward or backward with a greater force than the force that is used to turn it. The screw, therefore, is a kind of simple machine or force magnifier (see MACHINE, SIMPLE).

There are many forms of screws. A wood screw is used to join two pieces of material, such as wood, together. As the screw is turned, it moves forward, pulling the pieces of wood together with great force. Another form of screw is the nut and bolt. A nut and bolt grips objects together tightly as the nut is turned around the bolt. The objects are pulled together with a greater force than is used to turn the nut. A jackscrew uses the screw mechanism to lift a car. A handle is used to turn the screw of the jack. This produces a force large enough to lift the car.

The screw is a kind of wedge or inclined plane (see INCLINED PLANE). Raising an object by pushing a wedge under it is easier than lifting the object directly. The force used to push the wedge under the object produces a larger force, which raises the object. In the case of a jackscrew, the thread acts as a wedge wrapped around a cylinder. Turning the handle moves the thread under the car, as if a wedge was being pushed under the car. In the wood screw, the thread cuts into the wood as the screw is turned, as if a wedge was pulling the wood with great force.

PROJECT 50

SCREW

There are many kinds of screws and bolts, each designed for a particular purpose. Pictured here are (1) a round head slotted wood screw, (2) a flat head Phillips wood screw, (3) a flat head slotted wood screw, (4) a hexagonal head bolt, and (5) a bolt for use with a hexagonal wrench.

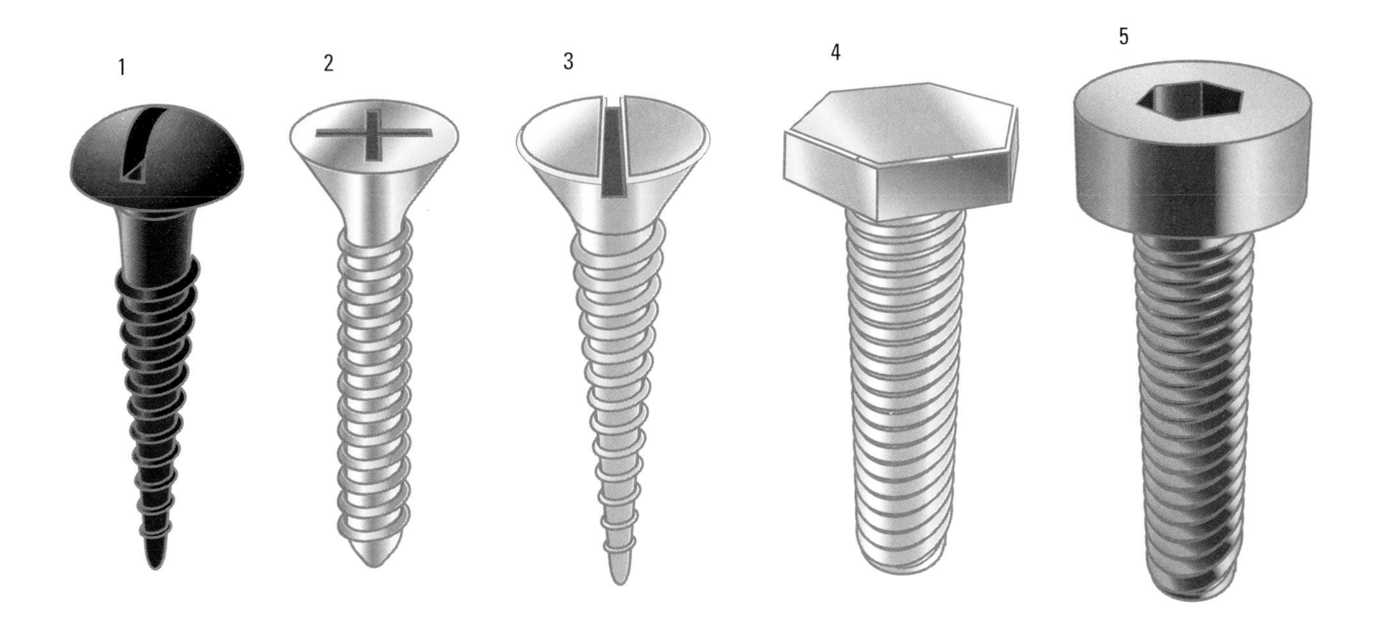

SCURVY (skûr′vē) Scurvy is a disease caused by a lack of vitamin C (ascorbic acid) in the diet. Its symptoms include swelling and bleeding of the gums; loose teeth; sore, stiff joints and legs; and bleeding under the skin. In infants, the legs swell and are painful when bent, and disorders of the bones often occur.

For many years, scurvy was a common problem among sailors and other people who lacked a balanced diet. The connection between scurvy and diet was not firmly established until the 1700s. By that time, people came to realize that scurvy could be avoided by including oranges, lemons, and other citrus fruits, as well as cabbage, in the diet (see CITRUS FRUIT).

Today, scurvy is very rare in industrialized countries. Even severe cases of scurvy can be cured in several days by moderate doses of vitamin C.
See also DEFICIENCY DISEASES; NUTRITION; VITAMIN.

SEA A sea is a large body of salt water. Though the word *sea* is often given the same meaning as ocean, more strictly it is an area smaller than an ocean and usually lies over a continental shelf close to land (see CONTINENTAL SHELF; OCEAN). Often the boundaries of a particular sea are defined by peninsulas or island chains, such as the Sea of Japan, which lies between the islands of Japan, the Asian mainland, and the peninsula of Korea. Large lakes in continental areas are often termed "inland seas." These include the Caspian Sea and the Dead Sea.

SEA ANEMONE (sē ə nĕm′ə nē) The sea anemone is a soft-bodied sea animal belonging to the group known as coelenterates or cnidarians (see CNIDARIA). The sea anemone is closely related to the jellyfishes and corals. The animal is so named because it looks like the anemone, a kind of flower. The base of the sea anemone's body may stick to an underwater rock, to which it remains attached. Some sea anemones fasten themselves to the shells of crabs and share the crabs' wanderings. This relationship is symbiotic, since the crab is protected by the sea anemone which, in turn, shares the meals caught by the crab (see SYMBIOSIS).

The sea anemone's mouth is surrounded by a cluster of slender, brightly colored growths called tentacles, which look like flower petals. The animal uses its tentacles to catch food and draw it into its mouth. The tentacles are armed with tiny poisonous stingers that numb small fish, crabs, and shrimp so they can be easily swallowed.

Sea anemones are found in great ocean depths and along rocky seacoasts, such as the North Atlantic coast, and in harbors. The animals are found in concentrated numbers wherever a strong current exists. Anemones gather near such currents because the flow of the water helps bring an abundance of food within their reach. Many sea anemones live between the tide levels. They survive when the tide goes out by pulling in their tentacles, closing their mouths, and contracting into rounded blobs of jelly.

Sea anemones reproduce sexually, and also asexually by budding. In budding, the new animal grows out from the base of the parent's body, finally breaking off and forming a new individual.
See also BUDDING; REPRODUCTION.

SEA ANEMONE
Unlike most fishes, a clown fish is not harmed by the stinging tentacles of a sea anemone because the skin of the fish is covered by slimy mucus.

SEABORG, GLENN THEODORE (1912–) Glenn Seaborg is an American chemist who was born in Ishpeming, Michigan, and is known for his work in making elements. He was one of a team of scientists who made plutonium in 1940. Later, he led the team of scientists who made a number of new elements that are called the actinides (see ELEMENT). There are sixteen actinide elements, each having an atomic number between 89 and 105. The actinides include americium, curium, berkelium, californium, einsteinium, fermium, mendelevium, and nobelium. In 1951, Seaborg shared the Nobel Prize for physics with Edwin McMillan for work on the elements.

Seaborg was chancellor of the University of California at Berkeley in 1958. He was chairman of the U.S. Atomic Energy Commission (now the Nuclear Regulatory Commission) from 1961 to 1971. Seaborg has been associate director of the Lawrence Berkeley Laboratories for over twenty years. His many honors and awards include the National Medal of Science, won in 1991.

SEA CUCUMBER The sea cucumber is an animal that is related to sea urchins and starfish. It belongs to the phylum Echinodermata (see ECHINODERMATA). The sea cucumber's body looks much like a garden cucumber. It ranges in length from 1 to 80 in. [2.5 to 200 cm]. A mouth opening is at one end of the body. Around the mouth is a ring of slender, branching growths called tentacles, usually numbering ten or more. These tentacles expand and contract as the animal searches for and picks up its food. Sea cucumbers feed mainly on debris (edible materials floating in the water). Some gather it from the seabed with their tentacles, while others use their tentacles like nets to catch the debris as it falls. Most species have five double rows of tube feet, which can be extended and used for burrowing or crawling over the seabed.

There are more than 1,000 species of sea cucumbers found in all the oceans. They live mostly in shallow water, but sometimes they are found at great depths. Sea cucumbers can detach and throw out their intestines when another animal attacks them. The intestines interfere with the movements of attackers, allowing the sea cucumber to escape its enemies. The sea cucumber then grows a new set of internal organs.

South Sea islanders place sea cucumber juices in water to kill or stun fish. However, fluids from the sea cucumber are not toxic (poisonous) to humans. In fact, sea cucumbers are used in making soup in China.

SEA CUCUMBER

The sea cucumber's mouth is surrounded by a ring of tentacles, which the animal uses to pick up scraps of food.

SEA HORSE A sea horse is an unusual looking saltwater fish that belongs to the family Syngnathidae. It is closely related to the pipefish (see FISH; PIPEFISH).

Sea horses are so named because their head looks like a horse's head. Sea horses are only a few inches long. They swim holding the body in a vertical position, with the head facing forward.

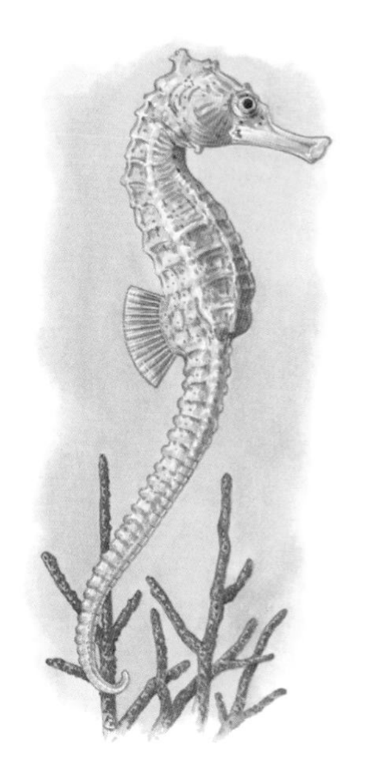

SEA HORSE

Sea horses swim upright in the water or anchor themselves by coiling their tails around weeds or coral. This male sea horse is carrying eggs in its belly pouch.

Five species of sea horses live along the coast of North America. Sea horses live in shallow, coastal areas. They hide in seaweed to which they cling with their tails. Sea horses have an unusual way of reproducing (see REPRODUCTION). The females lay their eggs in pouches in the males' bellies. The eggs develop inside the pouches.

SEAL A seal is a warm-blooded, hairy mammal that has become adapted to life in the sea (see MAMMAL). Eared seals, such as fur seals and sea lions, belong to the family Otariidae (see SEA LION). Earless seals, or true seals, such as harbor seals and elephant seals, belong to the family Phocidae (see ELEPHANT SEAL). Walruses, a third group of seals, belong to the family Odobenidae.

Millions of years ago, the seal was a land animal. In adapting to life in the water, the seal's feet and legs evolved into flippers. Its body became streamlined. It is covered with oily, gray or brown fur. This oily fur helps the seal slide through the water and keeps water from penetrating the fur down to the skin. Just under the skin, the seal has a thick layer of spongy, fatty tissue called blubber. This blubber keeps in the seal's body heat when it swims in cold water. Most species of seals are adapted to life in polar regions, and most of them live in the Arctic.

Seals are fast swimmers for short distances, and many of them can stay under the water for up to thirty minutes searching for food. Seals feed on fish, squid, and other sea animals. Seals range in size from the ringed seal, which is about 5 ft. [1.5 m] long and up to 240 lb. [110 kg] in weight, to the elephant seal, which can be up to 20 ft. [6 m] long and 6,050 lb. [2,750 kg] in weight.

Earless seals have no outer ears. Instead, they have an opening on each side of the head leading down to the eardrums. Their front flippers are short, and in the water they are used only for steering. Most of the time they are held close to the body. The two rear flippers are held together and waved from side to side to move the seal through the water, just as a fish swims by waving its tail from side to side. On land, earless seals move about clumsily by contracting their belly muscles.

Eared seals have small outer ears. Their front flippers are comparatively long, and they are used like oars to move the seals through the water. The rear flippers are used as rudders for steering. The rear flippers can be turned forward under the body, allowing the seals to move quickly on land.

All seals come ashore to have their babies, or pups, although some babies are born in shallow pools at low tide. Some pups can swim almost immediately, but most species spend two or three weeks on the shore before their coats are ready for them to take to the water. Eared seals and some earless seals breed in large colonies.

Every summer, thousands of fur seals journey to

SEAL—Layer of fat

Earless seals, or true seals, have weak flippers and move on land by flexing their belly muscles. A thick layer of fat, called blubber, keeps out the cold. Pictured here are (1) a hooded seal, (2) a harp seal, (3) a bearded seal, and (4) a ribbon seal.

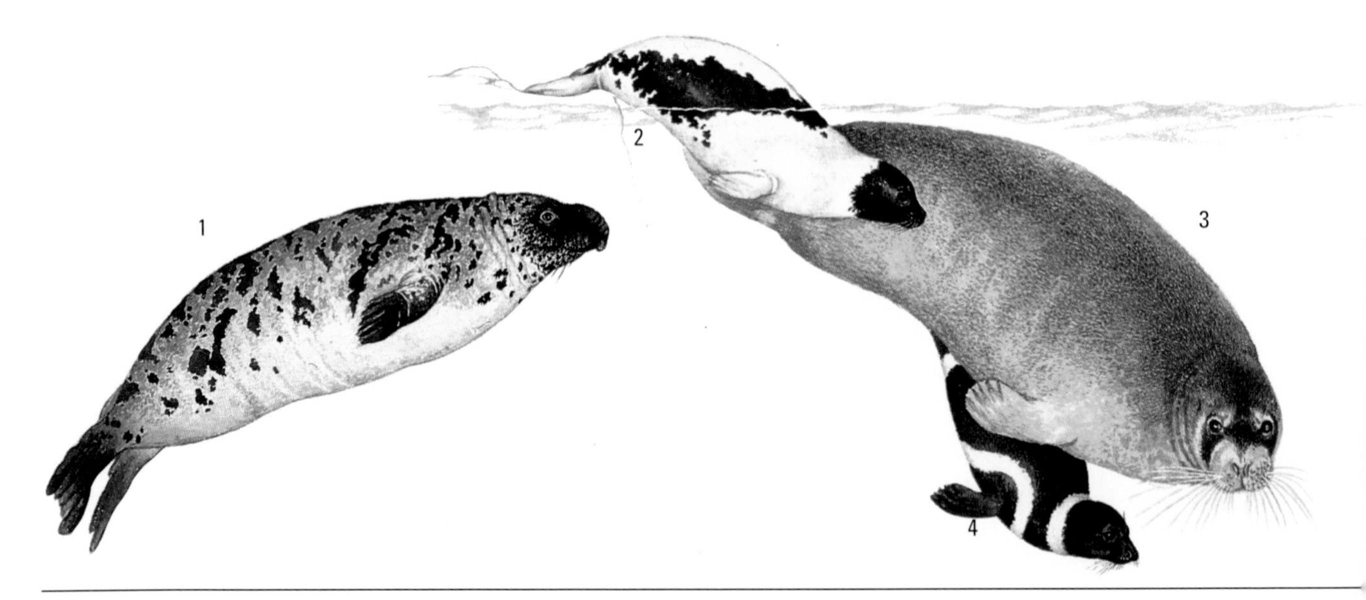

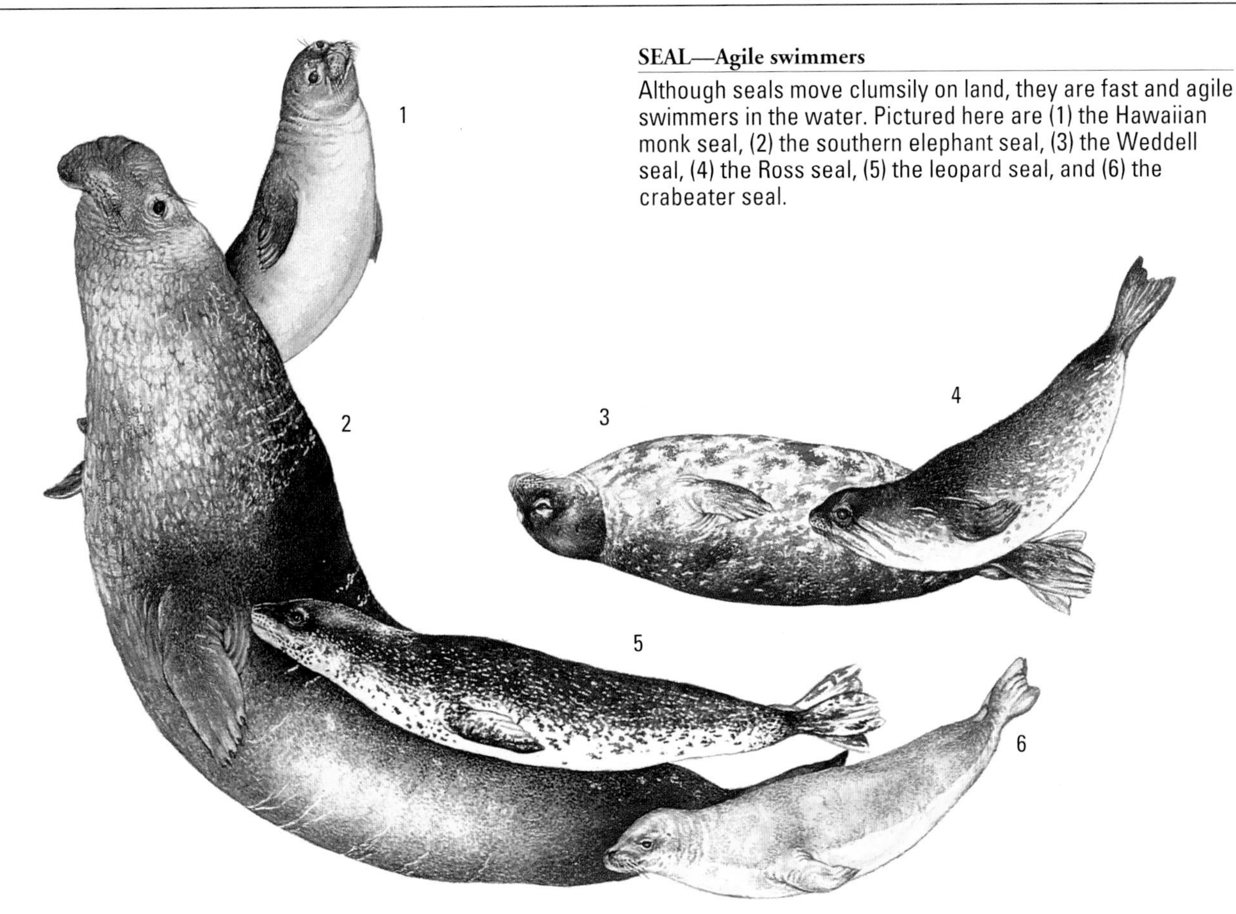

SEAL—Agile swimmers

Although seals move clumsily on land, they are fast and agile swimmers in the water. Pictured here are (1) the Hawaiian monk seal, (2) the southern elephant seal, (3) the Weddell seal, (4) the Ross seal, (5) the leopard seal, and (6) the crabeater seal.

the Pribilof Islands in the North Pacific to breed. This seal rookery, as it is called, is the largest seal breeding ground in the world.

Eskimos and other seal hunters from various countries kill many thousands of seals each year. Their fur is used to make coats and other garments. Seal meat is used in fertilizer and poultry food.

SEALAB Sealab was an oceanographic research program conducted by the United States Navy to find out whether people can live and work on the sea floor in the relatively shallow waters of the continental shelf (see CONTINENTAL SHELF). Scientists called aquanauts lived in underwater chambers called habitats for various lengths of time. After they returned to the surface, they were tested to see what effects the experience had had on them.

In 1964, the Sealab I habitat was set at a depth of about 200 ft. [60 m]. Four aquanauts spent eleven days in Sealab I. They left Sealab for several hours each day to work on the ocean floor. In 1965, Sealab II was placed at a depth of 205 ft. [62.5 m], and twenty-eight aquanauts spent fifteen-day periods in it. In 1968, Sealab III, an international cooperation involving divers from Britain, Canada, and Australia as well as the United States, was placed at a depth of 600 ft. [180 m]. Five eight-person teams each spent twelve days in it. It was found that the aquanauts suffered greatly from cold when outside the habitat, and the Sealab III experiment ended when one of the aquanauts died.

In 1969, the United States launched a scientific program using a habitat called Tektite, which was designed to allow aquanauts to stay on the ocean floor for up to sixty days and to carry out extensive research in marine biology. The two-chamber, four-room habitat provided a combination of laboratory and living quarters. It was placed at a depth of 50 ft. [15 m] in the Caribbean waters off the Virgin Islands. In 1970, ten five-person teams took part in the program over a seven-month period. From this work, Tektite aquanauts learned many new things about the ecology of coral reefs and the living habits of the marine life that inhabits the reefs.

See also CORAL; DIVING; MARINE BIOLOGY; OCEANOGRAPHY.

SEA LION The sea lion is a very agile (able to move easily) type of seal that belongs to the family Otariidae (see SEAL). The sea lion is an eared seal. The males, with the exception of the California sea lion, have manes. Sea lions feed mainly on squid, octopus, and fish. They breed in large herds. Baby sea lions are called pups. They are born after a gestation period of one year (see GESTATION PERIOD). In some regions, sea lions are hunted for their meat, blubber, and hides. Their fur is yellowish to brown.

Steller's sea lion, also called the northern sea lion, is a large species. Males are about 11 ft. [3.3 m] in length and weigh about 2,200 lb. [1,000 kg]. The California sea lion is a smaller species, with the males reaching a maximum length of about 8 ft. [2.5 m] and weighing up to 600 lb. [270 kg].

SEA LION

Unlike true seals, a sea lion has ear flaps on the sides of its head behind the eyes. Sea lions are good swimmers, but they cannot hold their breath underwater as long as true seals. A female Steller's sea lion is illustrated.

SEA SLUG The sea slug, or nudibranch, is a marine gastropod that lacks a shell and mantle cavity (see GASTROPOD). It also lacks true gills, although the body surface has many fingerlike outgrowths that help to absorb oxygen from the water. These outgrowths, called cerata, are often brilliantly colored. Antennalike organs called rhinophores grow from the head. Sea slugs are found in shallow waters, where they feed on sea anemones and various other sea animals. Sea slugs are not bothered by the stingers of sea anemones. Some species of sea slugs even take these stingers into their own tissues as defense organs.

SEA SLUG

Sea slugs are shell-less gastropod mollusks that live in shallow waters, where they feed mainly on sea anemones.

SEA SNAKE The sea snake is any of about fifty species of venomous (poisonous) snakes that have adapted to life in the sea (see SNAKE). These animals have flattened, oarlike tails, and their bodies are also slightly flattened from side to side. Their nostrils have valvelike closings, usually on top of the snout. Most sea snakes are about 3 to 4 ft. [1 to 1.3 m] in length.

Most sea snakes are found along the coasts of Australia and Asia. One species, the yellow-bellied sea snake, is found throughout the Pacific Ocean. A few sea snakes lay eggs on land, but the majority bear live young at sea. Sea snakes feed mainly on fish.

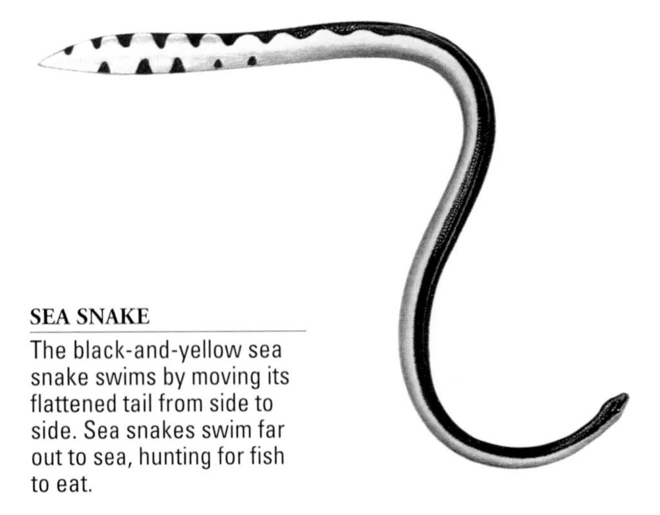

SEA SNAKE

The black-and-yellow sea snake swims by moving its flattened tail from side to side. Sea snakes swim far out to sea, hunting for fish to eat.

SEASON

A season is a division of the year characterized by certain weather (see WEATHER). In the temperate regions of the globe, as in North America and Europe, there are four seasons: spring, summer, fall (or autumn), and winter. In the Northern Hemisphere, spring begins on the vernal equinox, March 20 or 21, when the sun is directly over the equator. Summer begins on the summer solstice, June 20 or 21, when the sun reaches its northernmost point. Fall begins on the autumnal equinox, September 22 or 23, when the sun is again directly over the equator. Winter begins on the winter solstice, December 21 or 22, when the sun reaches its southernmost point. The seasons are reversed in the Southern Hemisphere, with winter beginning in June and summer beginning in December (see EQUINOX; SOLSTICE).

The seasons are a result of the earth's tilt on its axis, an imaginary line running from pole to pole. During the six months that the North Pole is tilted toward the sun, the Northern Hemisphere receives more sunlight than the Southern Hemisphere does. The greater hours of sunlight result in more heating of the atmosphere and thus warmer weather. During this time, the seasons that include late spring, summer, and early fall occur in the Northern Hemisphere. When the South Pole is tilted toward the sun, the Northern Hemisphere receives less sunlight and thus less heat. The weather becomes cooler, and the seasons of late fall, winter, and early spring occur in the Northern Hemisphere.

Throughout most of the United States, the four seasons are quite distinct. The summers are rather warm, the winters are cold, and spring and fall are somewhat mild. In the tropics, where the sun is strong the entire year, the seasons are usually distinguished by rainfall. Often, rain occurs during certain months of the year (the rainy season), while the rest of the year is dry (the dry season). In monsoon areas, such as India, where the climate is controlled by winds to and from the Indian Ocean, there are three seasons—cold, hot, and rainy. The polar regions are characterized by a short summer and a long, bitterly cold winter. The change between winter and summer in polar regions is so abrupt that there are only two distinct seasons. During the summer in the polar regions, the sun does not set for several months.

See also CLIMATE; MIDNIGHT SUN.

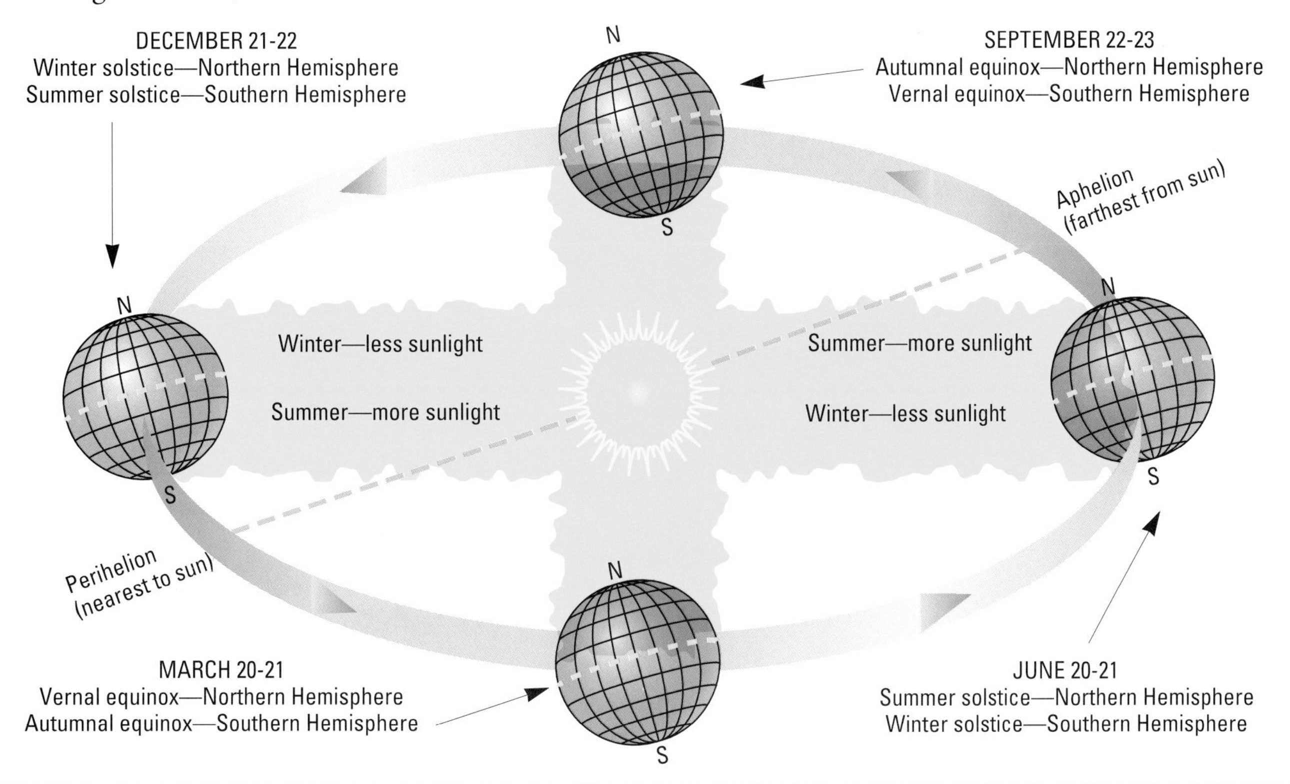

SEA SQUIRT The sea squirt, or ascidian, is a type of invertebrate with some primitive vertebrate features (see INVERTEBRATE; VERTEBRATE). These features include a notochord in the tail of the free-swimming larva (see LARVA; NOTOCHORD). There are over 1,000 species, and they are found in all the oceans. The animals often attach themselves to pier pilings, ships, crabs, and large seashells. Some species of sea squirts live in colonies, or large groups. Other species are solitary.

The sea squirt looks like a lump of jelly. Its body has a tunic (outer protective covering). There are two large pores (openings) in this covering. One pore takes water into the body. The other forces water out of the body. When the animal is disturbed, it squirts the water out quite violently, thus giving the sea squirts their name. Water taken into the body is filtered through the sievelike gills, which absorb oxygen and also trap small food particles.

SEA SQUIRT
Sea squirts have two body openings. One opening takes in water, which is squirted out of the other opening.

All adults have both male and female reproductive organs. However, eggs shed into the water are fertilized by sperm from another individual. Reproduction may also occur by budding (see BUDDING; HERMAPHRODITE; REPRODUCTION). In some forms, fingerlike projections form buds, break off, and settle elsewhere to become new individuals.

SEA URCHIN (sē ûr′chĭn) The sea urchin is an echinoderm with a body shaped like a ball that is slightly flattened at the top and bottom (see ECHINODERMATA). The sea urchin's body is covered with limestone plates that are embedded in the skin. These plates have hinged spines that protect the animal from its enemies. The spines are so sharp that they can pierce a person's foot if he or she steps on a sea urchin.

Between the spines there are many tiny tube feet. These enable the sea urchin to move about, and they are also used to capture food. The tube feet have sucking disks. The sea urchin thrusts the tube feet through tiny holes in the body covering. The mouth is on the underside of the body. In many sea urchins there are five pointed teeth set in a complicated "cage" of muscles and limestone plates. This is called Aristotle's lantern. It is used to scrape algae and other food from rocks and to grind up the food.

Sea urchins are found on rocky shores, in sand, and in deep water. A type of sea urchin found on the California coast can burrow into solid rock. Burrowing forms usually strain food particles from the sand and water with their tube feet. Sea urchins scatter eggs or sperm from pores in the upper surface of their body, and fertilization takes place in the water. The young urchins pass through several floating stages before they reach maturity.

SEAWEED Seaweeds are algae that live in the oceans (see ALGAE). Most species live in shallow coastal waters. In cooler waters, long, brown algae (phylum Phaeophyta) are most plentiful. In warmer and tropical waters, long, red algae (phylum Rhodophyta) are more common. Gulfweed, or sargasso weed, is a brown alga with many small air bladders that help keep it afloat (see SARGASSO). Giant kelp is a large brown alga that lives in the Pacific Ocean. It sometimes reaches a length of 200 ft. [60 m].

Seaweeds have many uses. Some species supply algin, a food additive. Algin helps keep liquids that have been mixed together from separating. For example, algin is added to ice cream to prevent ice crystals from forming. It is also used in salad dressings and chocolate milk. Agar is prepared from another species of seaweed. Among other uses, agar is used in laboratories as a culture medium (food) for growing microorganisms (see AGAR). Seaweeds are rich in iodine and other minerals. They are sometimes used as fertilizers (see FERTILIZER). Many scientists believe that, in the near future, seaweed may be a major source of food for people throughout the world.

SEAWEED
This seaweed is called bladder wrack after the small air bladders that help keep it afloat.

SEDATIVE (sĕd′ə tĭv) A sedative is a drug that reduces tension or induces sleep. Sedatives work by depressing, or slowing down, the activity of the central nervous system (see DRUG; NERVOUS SYSTEM). Some sedatives are taken in small doses throughout the day to help relieve nervousness or anxiety. Sedatives may also be taken in larger doses at night to help a person sleep.

Until the late 1800s, alcohol and opium were the two most widely used sedatives. Barbiturates are sedatives that were once widely prescribed in the 1950s and 1960s. However, they are not prescribed as much today (see BARBITURATE). Today, most sedatives belong to a class of drugs known as benzodiazepines.

Sedatives are powerful drugs. They can cause great harm if they are used without supervision by a medical doctor. However, if used in small doses for a limited period of time under a physician's supervision, sedatives can be safe and helpful. Carefully administered sedatives are sometimes used to treat minor mental disorders. Sedatives are often used with other drugs to help produce anesthesia before surgery (see ANESTHETIC). In some cases, sedatives are used to help relieve withdrawal symptoms caused by alcohol or drug addiction (see ADDICTION).

In large doses, however, sedatives can cause unconsciousness, coma, and death. Long-term use of sedatives, even in small doses, can lead to addiction. Addiction to a sedative, particularly to a benzodiazepine or barbiturate, is even more dangerous than addiction to a narcotic (see NARCOTIC). Sudden withdrawal from a sedative often causes severe convulsions and may result in death.

Most people who use sedatives for an extended period of time develop a tolerance to the drug. This means that they need increasingly larger doses of the drug to get the same effect. Some people have a paradoxical reaction to certain sedatives. This means that instead of being calmed, they become highly excited. In these cases, the doctor stops the use of the sedative and may substitute another drug to get the desired effect.
See also TRANQUILIZER.

SEDGE FAMILY The sedge family, Cyperaceae, includes ninety genera (plural of *genus*) and four thousand species of monocotyledonous herbaceous plants (see HERBACEOUS PLANT; MONOCOTYLEDON). Most of these grasslike plants are found in damp places throughout the world. Unlike the grasses, however, members of this family have solid stems that are often triangular in section. The leaves, when present, are arranged in three rows, and their bases are wrapped around the stem. Tiny brown flowers grow in spikes, or clusters (see FLOWER; INFLORESCENCE; PLANT KINGDOM). The spikes are made of either male flowers or female flowers. The sexes may be on one plant (monoecious) or on different plants (dioecious) (see MONOECIOUS). Members of this family range in height from about 1 in. [2.5 cm] to 13.3 ft. [4 m].

The sedge family probably evolved from primitive members of the rush family (see RUSH). Many sedges are called rushes. The bulrush, for

SEDGE FAMILY

The sedge called hard rush (left) grows in damp places near marshes and rivers.

example, is a member of the sedge family. Like the rushes, bulrushes are used in weaving baskets and chair seats.

SEDIMENTARY ROCK Sedimentary (sĕd′ə mĕn′tə rē) rock is formed from the accumulation of sediment under water or on land. These deposits of sediment include loose sand and pebbles as well as the remains of dead plants and animals. Pressure from above causes the material to harden into rock. The hardening process takes many thousands of years.

Sedimentary rock occurs in layers called strata. The strata are important in both geology and biology because of their rich supply of fossils (see FOSSIL). The ages of different strata are sometimes determined by comparing the fossils they contain.

Although sedimentary rock covers 75 percent of the earth's surface, it only accounts for 5 percent of the earth's crust. Igneous and metamorphic rocks make up the remaining 95 percent of the earth's crust (see IGNEOUS ROCK; METAMORPHIC ROCK).

Sedimentary rocks are classified according to the material from which they formed. Some sedimentary rocks are composed of rock fragments cemented together. This type is called clastic sedimentary rock. Clastic rocks are the indirect result of erosion. Larger rocks are broken up by water, glaciers, and other agents of erosion (see EROSION). The fragments are deposited in layers that eventually harden into rocks. This rock-forming process is called lithification. During lithification, water is pressed out from between the rock fragments, and the fragments are bound together by new minerals. Types of clastic sedimentary rock include conglomerates, shale, and sandstone (see CONGLOMERATE; SANDSTONE; SHALE).

Chemical sedimentary rock forms from minerals that were once dissolved in water. After the water evaporates, the minerals crystallize. Sedimentary rocks formed this way include gypsum and some kinds of limestone (see GYPSUM; LIMESTONE).

Organic sedimentary rock forms from the remains of dead plants and animals. These remains include shells, skeletons, and other organic matter. Many types of limestone, such as the chalky limestone of the White Cliffs of Dover in England, are organic sedimentary rocks. Coal, which forms from decayed organic matter, is also an organic sedimentary rock.

See also COAL; ROCK; ROCK CYCLE.

SEDIMENTARY ROCK

Sedimentary rock, such as this sandstone cliff in Baja California, Mexico, occurs in layers called strata.

A seed contains an embryo plant that developed from a fertilized egg. The seed developed from the ovule that contained the egg (see EMBRYO; FERTILIZATION; POLLINATION). Most seeds also have an endosperm and a seed coat. The endosperm contains a store of food, which is used by the embryo. The food consists of fats, proteins, and carbohydrates, especially starch. The endosperm is formed at the same time that the egg is fertilized (see ENDOSPERM). The seed coat develops from the wall of the ovule. It may be thick or thin, depending on the species of plant. The function of the seed coat is to protect the embryo and to keep moisture from escaping from the seed. Among the angiosperms, or flowering plants, the seed is enclosed by a fruit that develops from the mature ovary (see ANGIOSPERM; FLOWER; FRUIT). Among gymnosperms, which are mostly cone-bearing plants, the seed sits on a scale of the cone (see CONIFER; GYMNOSPERM). Seeds are the major reproductive structures of all higher plants.

The embryo is a tiny plant. It has one or more leaves called cotyledons (see COTYLEDON). The embryo gradually absorbs food from the endosperm. The embryo needs this food as an energy source as it begins to grow. If all the food in the endosperm is absorbed by the embryo before the seed is ripe, the seed is said to be nonendospermic. If only part of the food is absorbed, the seed is endospermic. Food taken from the endosperm is initially stored in the cotyledons. The seeds of angiosperms have one or two cotyledons. Plants that have seeds with one cotyledon are called monocotyledons (see MONOCOTYLEDON). Plants that have seeds with two cotyledons are called dicotyledons (see DICOTYLEDON). Conifers may have between eight and twenty cotyledons.

SEED VARIETY

The seeds of the gladdon (above), also called stinking iris, are carried inside bright red berries. The berries smell like rotten meat and attract animals that eat the berries and scatter the seeds in their droppings. The seeds of the dandelion (left) are attached to small, fluffy "parachutes" that are scattered widely by the wind.

In addition to the cotyledons, an embryo has a tiny root called a radicle and a tiny stem called a plumule. When these structures start to grow, they use some of the stored food. The radicle grows into a root that begins absorbing water and minerals. The plumule grows into a shoot that produces leaves. Once the leaves have formed, they start making their own food through photosynthesis (see PHOTOSYNTHESIS).

The sprouting of a seed is called germination (see GERMINATION). Most seeds require a certain temperature in order to germinate. Many require a period of low temperatures before they can germinate at a higher temperature. This period of inactivity is called dormancy (see DORMANCY). During dormancy, a seed uses its stored food supplies at a very slow rate. Some seeds germinate in the spring as soon as the soil begins to warm. Others germinate in the summer, when the soil is hotter. However, other seeds may germinate as soon as they are released from the parent plant. Some even germinate while still attached to the parent.

Oxygen and water are also required for germination. Oxygen gives the seed the ability to change food into energy. This energy is used for growing. Water causes many changes in the seed. As the seed absorbs water, its coat softens, and its inner tissues swell. The embryo breaks through the seed coat as it grows. The radicle grows downward into the soil. A network of delicate root hairs develops from the radicle. These hairs take up minerals and water. As the radicle grows downward, the plumule pushes upward toward the light.

Seeds vary greatly in size, shape, and appearance. Some, such as those of the orchid family, are so small that they can hardly be seen with the naked eye. Others, such as those of a type of coconut, are huge and may weigh more than 40 lb. [18 kg].

When they are mature, the seeds must be dispersed, or scattered, so that they will all have a chance to grow. There are several means of dispersal (see DISPERSION OF PLANTS). Some seeds are light or have special feathery or winglike structures that allow them to float on the wind. Some have waterproof seed coats, or "shells," and float in the water. Some fruits and seeds are enclosed in fruits that are eaten by animals. The animals spit out the seeds or scatter them in their droppings. Some fruits and seeds are sticky or have burrs, which also attach to animals that disperse them.

Seeds are used widely as foods. Bread, breakfast cereal, and pasta are usually made from the seeds of corn, barley, oats, rice, rye, and wheat (see CEREAL CROP). Legume seeds, such as beans, peanuts, and peas, are important foods around the world (see LEGUME). Livestock eat seed mixtures. Seeds contain oils that are extracted and used in cooking. Some of the most common oils from seeds are corn, peanut, sesame, soy, and sunflower. Seed oils are also used in paints, soaps, and wood finishes. Seeds of the coffee and cacao plants are used to make beverages.

PROJECT 62, 72

DEWBERRY SEEDS

The dewberry bears compound fruits called drupelets, each of which contains a single seed. When ripe, the fruits are eaten by birds, which scatter the seeds.

SEISMOLOGY (sīz mŏl′ə jē) Seismology is the study of earthquakes and seismic, or earthquake, waves (see EARTHQUAKE). Seismologists use an instrument called a seismograph to record the time and intensity of seismic waves generated by an earthquake. Such recordings are taken in several places to determine the epicenter, or point of origin, of an earthquake.

Seismology is also concerned with the properties of the materials that occur within the earth. Seismic waves can be produced by dynamite, bombs, and other artificial means. These "artificial" seismic waves help seismologists learn about the geophysical properties of faults, oceanic ridges, and other geological formations (see FAULT).

It was through seismology that scientists determined that the rocks composing the earth's crust and mantle are quite different (see EARTH). It is known that seismic waves suddenly change speed as they pass from the mantle into the crust. This led to the discovery of the Moho (Mohorovičić discontinuity), the boundary region between the mantle and the crust (see MOHO). Seismology also plays an important role in prospecting for petroleum and other substances.

See also GEOLOGY; PROSPECTING.

SELECTIVE BREEDING Selective breeding is the controlled breeding of plants or animals to produce individuals possessing one or more desirable characteristics (see BREEDING). It is often used to combine the useful features of two or more races in a single individual. It is also called artificial selection.

Selective breeding has been taking place for thousands of years, ever since people started farming and picking out the best plants to use as seeds for the following year. Now that we know how characteristics are passed from one generation to the next, selective breeding has become much more scientific. Plant breeders, for example, have produced today's high-yielding wheat varieties by selecting plants with large grains and cross-breeding them with plants known to have strong stalks and a high resistance to disease. Selective breeding has also led to many improvements in farm animals, such as quicker growth, leaner meat, and higher milk yields. These crossbred plants and animals are known as hybrids (see HYBRID).

But selective breeding can go wrong. In an attempt to increase honey yields in Brazil, a race of high-yielding African honey bees was imported during the 1950s. These bees were known to be more aggressive than the local bees, but it was hoped that interbreeding the two races would produce a hybrid with the tameness of the local bees and the high honey production of the African bees. Unfortunately, this did not work. Some of the African bees escaped and mated with the local bees, creating a population of "killer bees." These hybrids have killed many people and animals. The bees spread rapidly and reached Texas in the early 1990s.

See also GENETICS; HEREDITY.

SELF-POLLINATION Self-pollination is the transfer of pollen from the anther (part of the male structure) to the stigma (part of the female structure) of the same flower (see ANTHER; FLOWER; STIGMA). Cells from the pollen grain then grow into the pistil and fertilize the eggs (see PISTIL; POLLINATION). Most plants have developed ways to prevent self-pollination and encourage cross-pollination, which is pollination with pollen from another flower of the same kind. This is better for plants because it enables genes to mix and produce new, stronger, and possibly more efficient offspring (see GENE; GENETICS; HEREDITY). However, self-pollination often occurs toward the end of a flower's life if it has not been cross-pollinated. Some flowers, such as garden pea flowers, actually prevent cross-pollination by failing to open properly, denying access to "foreign" pollen. Violets and some other plants produce special nonopening flowers, called cleistogamous flowers, in the fall. These flowers always pollinate themselves and ensure that some seed is produced even if the earlier flowers have not been pollinated.

Plant breeders also use the term *self-pollination* to refer to the pollination of a flower by any other flower on the same plant. Cross-pollination would then be defined as pollination by pollen from another plant of the same kind.

SEMICONDUCTOR A semiconductor is a substance that has different resistances to the passage of an electric current under different circumstances (see RESISTANCE, ELECTRICAL). Semiconductors conduct electricity better than insulators but not as well as good conductors, such as metals (see CONDUCTION OF ELECTRICITY). This gives them their name, which means "half-conductors." How well semiconductors conduct electricity depends on their temperature. When a metal is heated, its resistance increases. However, when a semiconductor is heated, its resistance decreases. Thus, a heated semiconductor conducts electricity better than one that is cold.

Semiconductors are also sensitive to the energy of light. The greater the intensity of the light that shines on them, the better they conduct electricity. The effect that light and heat energy have on semiconductors makes them extremely useful. Semiconductors are used in photoelectric cells and in solar cells (see PHOTOELECTRIC CELL).

Semiconductors include the elements germanium, selenium, and silicon, and the compounds lead sulfide, silicon carbide, cadmium sulfide, lead telluride, gallium arsenide, and indium antimonide (see COMPOUND; ELEMENT). When the atoms of these materials absorb heat or light energy, the electrons become less tightly bound to their atoms. They now can conduct electric current more readily. The resistance of the material decreases. The electrons that carry electric current from one atom to another are called valence electrons (see ATOM; VALENCE).

Another special property of semiconductors is the way that they behave when they are joined to another material, which may be a metal or a different semiconductor. The junction between the different materials forms a boundary. It allows electricity to pass more easily in one direction than the other. This property is used in transistors and integrated circuits for various electronic devices (see INTEGRATED CIRCUIT; TRANSISTOR).

Special semiconductors are made artificially for different purposes. A natural semiconductor, such as the element germanium, is called an intrinsic semiconductor. Adding impurities to a natural

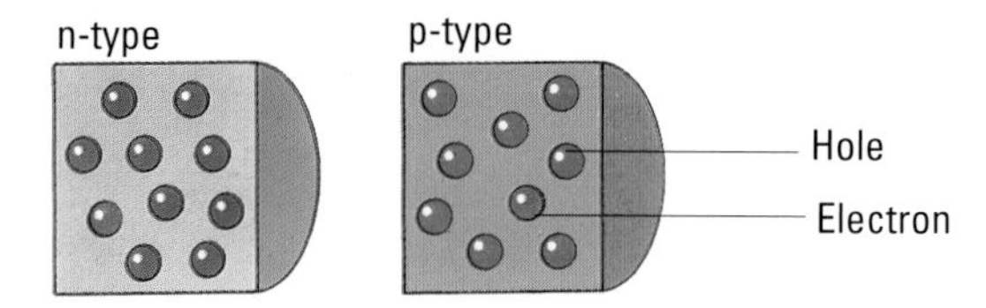

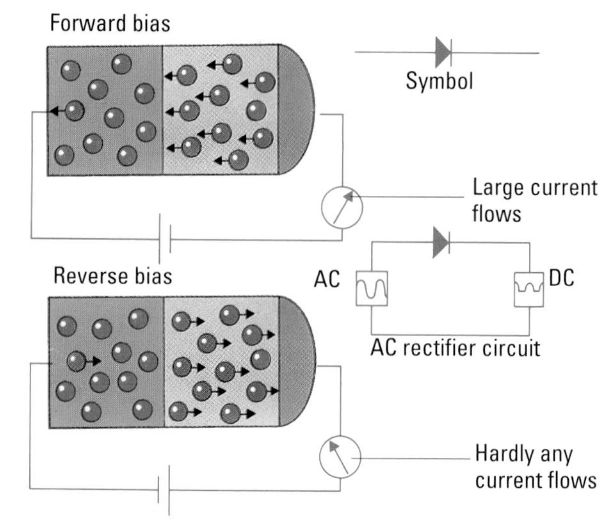

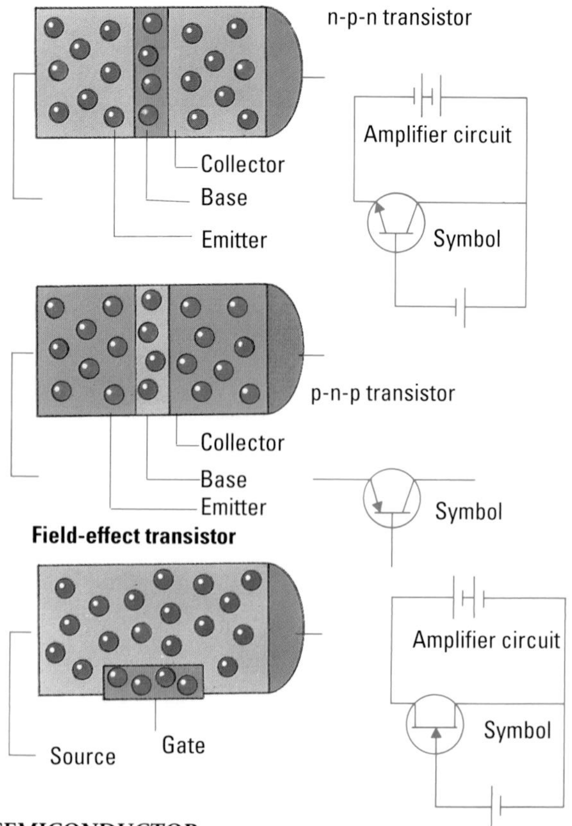

SEMICONDUCTOR
Semiconductor materials, such as silicon and gallium arsenide, are commonly used to make diodes and transistors. Diodes are employed to convert alternating current (AC) into direct current (DC). Transistors have many uses, including acting as amplifiers to "magnify" an electric current.

semiconductor produces another kind of semiconductor, an extrinsic semiconductor. This process of deliberately adding impurities is called "doping." There are two types of extrinsic semiconductors: a p-type semiconductor and an n-type semiconductor.

The *p* in *p-type* stands for "positive." In this type, the atoms of the impurity have fewer valence electrons than the pure substance around them. They accept electrons, which have a negative charge, from nearby atoms. This leaves the nearby atoms with a "hole" wherever an electron has been lost. This "hole" acts as a positive charge. If an electric current is passed through the material, electrons jump from one hole to another to carry the current.

The *n* in *n-type* stands for "negative." In this type of extrinsic semiconductor, there are no holes to act as positive electric charges. Instead, there are excess electrons that are not needed by the atoms of the impurity or by the nearby atoms of the pure semiconductor. These so-called free electrons have a negative charge. They can jump freely from one atom to another to carry an electric current.

By joining an n-type semiconductor with a p-type semiconductor at a junction, several useful electric devices can be made. Others can be made by making a "sandwich" of the two different types of semiconductors.

See also CURRENT, ELECTRIC; LED; SUPERCONDUCTIVITY.

SENSE In biology, a sense is a means of collecting information about the world and detecting changes within the body. The best-known senses are sight, hearing, taste, smell, and touch. These are known as the external senses because they give information about the outside world. Internal senses give information about the workings of the body. The internal senses include hunger, thirst, fatigue, pain, balance, and proprioception (the sense of bodily position and movement) (see PROPRIOCEPTION).

The senses begin to act when something stimulates special nerve cells called receptors in a sense organ. The receptors send nerve impulses along sensory nerves to the brain. When these signals reach the part of the brain called the cerebral cortex, we become conscious of the stimulus (see BRAIN; NERVE CELL; NERVOUS SYSTEM; RECEPTOR).

Different parts of the cerebral cortex are associated with each of the external senses. For example, the part for vision is at the back of the cerebral hemispheres. The part of the brain known as the hypothalamus is associated with some of the internal senses, including hunger and thirst. The cerebellum is associated with the senses of balance and proprioception.

See also EXTRASENSORY PERCEPTION; PERCEPTION.

PROJECT 63, 74

SENSITIVITY Sensitivity, also known as irritability, is one of the seven diagnostic features of living things. It is the ability of an organism to detect and respond to changes in its surroundings and also within its own body. In most animals, the changes are detected by special sense organs, such as the eyes or pressure-sensitive receptors in the skin (see SENSE). Plants lack obvious sense organs, but they can still pick up signals from the environment and respond accordingly. A plant receiving light from just one side, for example, bends in that direction (see MOVEMENT OF PLANTS). Sunflowers growing in an open field usually turn their heads to follow the sun during the day. Even the simplest organisms display some degree of sensitivity, even though they lack any sort of sense organs. Aquatic protozoans respond strongly to chemical stimulation, moving toward food extracts added to the water but turning away from acidic materials.

SENSOR Sensors are devices used to detect or measure different types of physical properties. There are many different kinds of sensors, each specially designed to measure a particular property, such as sound, pressure, light, heat, or chemical composition.

A mercury thermometer is an example of a simple type of sensor (see THERMOMETER). Here an increase in heat causes the mercury in the bulb to expand and move up a glass tube. The distance that the mercury moves can be correlated with the amount of temperature rise. Many other types of sensors work by converting a nonelectrical property into an electrical signal that varies as the property

being measured changes. The amount of change can then be calculated by measuring changes in the electrical current.
See also REMOTE SENSING.

SEPAL
The sepals of these chrysanthemum flowers are the green structures that surround the buds before they open.

SEPAL (sē'pəl) The sepals are the outermost parts of most flowers. The sepals protect the delicate developing flower. Once the flower opens, the sepals usually fold back or drop off. Most sepals are green and leaflike. Some, however, are brightly colored and are easily confused with the petals.
See also FLOWER.

SEPARATION In chemistry, separation is the splitting of a mixture of different substances into its components (see MIXTURE). Natural products from animals and plants, as well as human-made materials, occur in mixtures. Individual substances can be separated from mixtures in various ways. A soluble substance can be separated from an insoluble substance by filtration (see SOLUTION AND SOLUBILITY). The mixture is placed on a filter that retains (holds back) the insoluble substance and allows the solution of soluble substance, called the filtrate, to pass through (see FILTER; FILTRATION).

A soluble substance can be separated from other soluble substances by crystallization from a solution. One common method of obtaining crystals of a substance is allowing the solvent (water or some organic liquid) to evaporate (see EVAPORATION; SOLVENTS). Pure commercial sugar (sucrose) is separated from the many other compounds present in raw sugar by evaporating the solution (see SUCROSE). The sucrose crystallizes out, leaving the impurities in the liquid.

Liquids can be purified by distillation (see DISTILLATION). Solid impurities in water are removed by boiling the water and cooling the steam to obtain distilled water. Two or more liquids that have different boiling points can be separated by distillation through a fractionating column and a condenser (see CONDENSER). In the petroleum

SEPARATION
Rows of large filters are used to separate suspended solids from water at a water treatment plant. The filtered water is treated with chemicals to kill any germs and then pumped into the water supply system.

industry, fractional distillation is used to separate different products, such as gasoline, diesel fuel, and other liquids, from each other.

Chromatography is a process for separating and identifying the components of mixtures of substances. There are different types of chromatography (see CHROMATOGRAPHY). In paper chromatography, a drop of liquid containing the mixture is placed on a sheet of filter paper. A liquid is then allowed to flow over the spot and down the paper. Plant pigments can be separated in this way.

Column chromatography uses a glass or plastic tube filled with an absorbing material such as alumina. A solution of a mixture of substances is passed down the column followed by more of the same or another solvent. The individual components in the mixture travel down the column at different rates and are collected separately as the liquid flows out the bottom of the column. Chromatography is used in the pharmaceutical industry in the preparation of drugs.

PROJECT 5, 9, 21

SERPENTINE (sûr'pən tēn') Serpentine is a colorful, common rock-forming mineral that takes a high polish (see MINERAL; ROCK). It gets its name from its green and white mottled appearance, which resembles a serpent's (snake's) coloring. Its chemical composition is $Mg_3Si_2O_5\,(OH)_4$.

Serpentine occurs in two distinct forms: antigorite and chrysotile. Antigorite, a flaky variety, is found in massive rocks in many parts of the world. It is used as an ornamental stone to cover the outside of buildings. The largest deposit of chrysotile, the other variety of serpentine, is found in Ontario, Canada. Fibrous forms of chrysotile used to be the most important source of asbestos.
See also ASBESTOS.

SERUM (sîr'əm) Serum is the straw-colored, watery fluid left behind when blood clots. It is identical to plasma, except that it lacks fibrinogen (see BLOOD; PLASMA). Fibrinogen is a protein that is needed for blood to clot. Because serum contains no cells or clotting factors, it can be removed from one person and injected into another without causing clotting or other complications (see BLOOD TRANSFUSION; BLOOD TYPES).

Serum is mostly water. It also contains other substances, such as dissolved nutrients, wastes, minerals, hormones, and proteins. The most important of these proteins are the albumins and the globulins. The albumins help control the osmotic pressure of the blood (see OSMOSIS). In other words, they keep water from leaving the blood and entering the tissues.

The globulins include a group of proteins called the gamma globulins, or immunoglobulins. These proteins are antibodies, which give people immunity to diseases. Antibodies are produced in the blood in response to an infection (see ANTIBODY; IMMUNE SYSTEM; INFECTION). When a healthy person has recovered from an infection, his or her serum contains antibodies that were produced to fight that infection. Some of this serum can be removed and injected into someone else suffering from the same disease. The antibodies in the serum help the person's own immune system fight the infection. Serum used to treat infections caused by microorganisms is called antiserum (see MICROORGANISM). Serum used to treat infections caused by poisonous animal bites is called antivenin.

Antiserum may be given to an unvaccinated person who has been exposed to a certain disease, such as measles. The antiserum provides passive immunity. Although the active immunity produced by vaccination is more effective and longer lasting, passive immunity develops much more quickly (see VACCINATION). In some cases, such as rabies, both antiserum and vaccinations are used as treatment.
See also RABIES.

SERVAL (sûr'vəl) The serval is a slender, beautifully marked African cat. It has long legs and stands about 18 in. [45 cm] high. Its body is about 3 ft. [0.9 m] long. The serval's fur is yellow with black spots.

The serval lives in grasslands from the Cape of Good Hope in the south to Senegal and Sudan in the north. It hunts at night, feeding on fowl and other animals, including small antelopes. Its

SERVAL

The serval is a medium-size cat that lives in African grasslands. Its spotted coat makes it difficult to see in the grass.

large ears can swivel around and pick up the slightest sounds. The serval generally hunts on the ground, where its spotted coat provides excellent camouflage, but it is an expert climber and often climbs trees to hunt birds.

SET THEORY In mathematics, a set is a collection or group of items. If X is the set of natural numbers less than 6, we write: X = (1, 2, 3, 4, 5). 4 ⊂ X means that 4 is a member of the set X.

If one set is completely included in another set, we say is it a subset of the larger set. If Y = (natural numbers less than 100), then X is a subset of Y. This is written X ⊂ Y.

A Venn diagram represents sets as closed loops. The diagram following shows X as a subset of Y. That is, every number of the set X is also a member of the set Y.

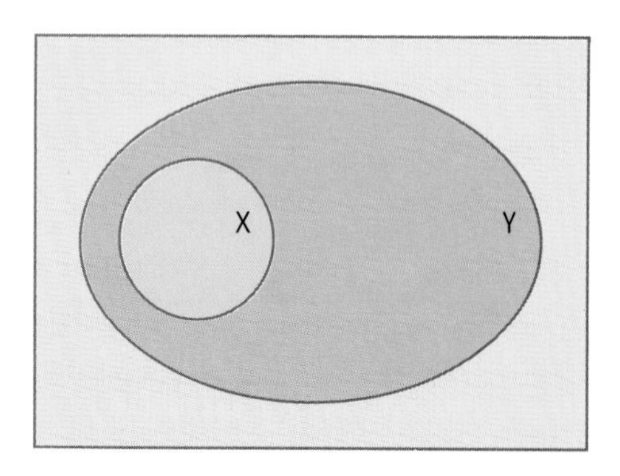

Sets can be combined in various ways. The intersection of two sets, A and B, is the set of items common to both A and B.

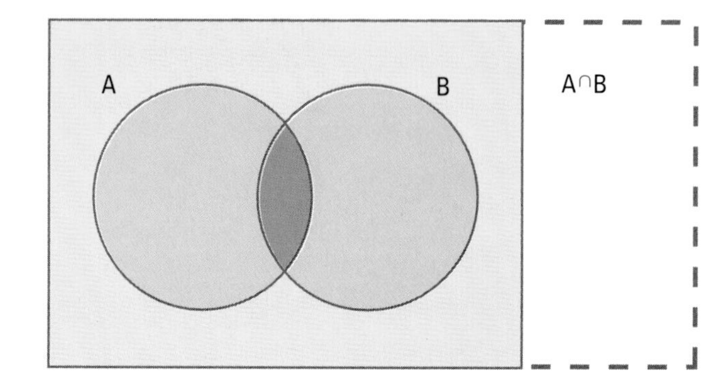

The overlapping dark blue part is the intersection, written A ∩B. The set of items belonging either to A or B or both is called the union of the two sets. It is written A ∪B.

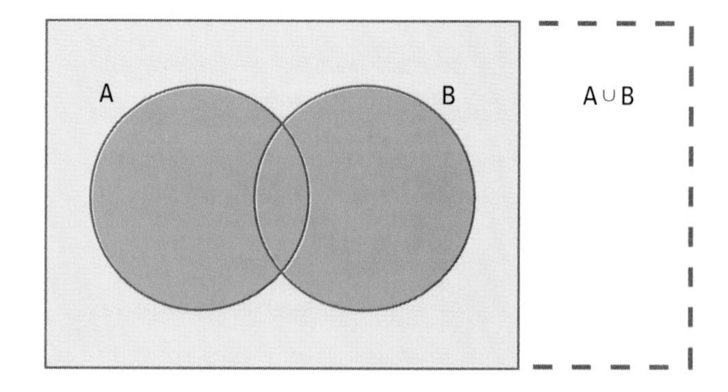

Example: A = (1, 2, 3, 4)
B = (2, 4, 6, 8)
A ∩B = (2, 4) and A ∪B = (1, 2, 3, 4, 6, 8)

If two sets do not overlap, then the intersection is an empty, or null, set, written Ø. If C = (8, 9, 10), then A ∩C = Ø.

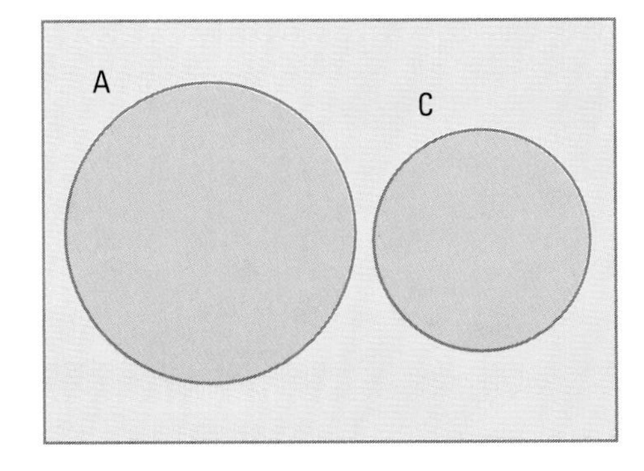

The set of items not belonging to A is called the complement of A, and is written A′.

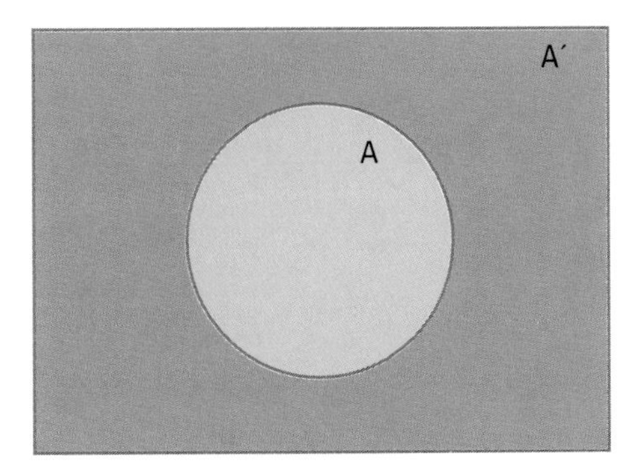

The theory of sets was invented in the nineteenth century by the German mathematician Georg Cantor. It has been used as a foundation on which all the laws of mathematics can be built.
See also MATHEMATICS.

SEWAGE TREATMENT (so͞o′ĭj trēt′mənt)

Sewage is a watery mixture of wastes that come from homes. It includes human wastes, soapy and dirty water from sinks and bathtubs, food scraps, and other garbage washed down drains. More than 90 percent of sewage is water used to wash the wastes away. A household can produce hundreds of gallons of sewage every day. There are two ways of disposing of this sewage. It can be stored in septic tanks in the ground until it soaks into the soil, or it can be dumped into bodies of water, such as rivers, lakes, and oceans.

Cities produce millions of gallons of sewage a day. There is not enough space in the ground for all of it, so cities are forced to dump the wastes into the water bodies. Unfortunately, this is a serious form of pollution (see POLLUTION). Human wastes contain bacteria and viruses that cause diseases. When these disease-causing microorganisms get into water, the water cannot be used safely for drinking or swimming. Also, the garbage in the sewage takes oxygen from the water as it decomposes (see DECOMPOSITION). In heavily polluted water, there is little oxygen, causing fish and other forms of water life to die. The only way to prevent this pollution is to treat—or clean up—the sewage before it is dumped into the water body.

Sewage may be carried from homes in underground pipes that lead to a sewage treatment plant. Once in the plant, the sewage undergoes primary treatment. Primary treatment removes the solid wastes by allowing them to sink to the bottom of a large tank. The liquid sewage is drained off the top, and the solid sewage is collected from the bottom and burned, composted, or dumped into a landfill. Some sewage plants provide only for primary treatment. The liquid sewage is then poured into the waterways. This liquid sewage, however, still contains bacteria, viruses, and other harmful wastes.

Most modern sewage treatment plants are equipped also for secondary treatment, which removes the harmful microorganisms and floating wastes. The sewage is mixed with bacteria that break down the wastes into harmless substances (see BACTERIA). Large amounts of chlorine are then mixed into the water to kill all remaining microorganisms (see CHLORINE). Sometimes other chemicals, such as ozone, are used instead (see OZONE LAYER).

Secondary treatment can be done in one of two ways. The activated sludge method mixes the liquid sewage with a thick, brown, mudlike sludge that contains helpful bacteria. Oxygen is pumped into the mixture to speed the decomposition. The mixture is then allowed to stand still, and the sludge sinks to the bottom. The sludge can then be reused. The water remaining on the top is clean and can be poured into the water body.

The other method of secondary treatment is called the trickling filter method. The liquid sewage is trickled through a deep bed of gravel. The gravel is coated with the helpful bacteria. The bacteria break down the sewage and, by the time the water reaches the bottom of the gravel, it is clean. It is collected in pipes and poured into the water body.

Many new treatment plants are adding a third step. In this step, nutrients and chemicals from the water are removed. Often, these chemicals can make the water undrinkable. They can also fertilize the water the same way fertilizers fertilize a lawn. They make water plants and algae grow much faster and more abundantly than they would otherwise. This abundant growth chokes off the water body into which the waste water is poured. After water has gone through the third step in a treatment plant, it is usually clean enough to drink.

A problem with many sewage treatment plants today is that the street sewers, which drain rain and snow off the streets, flow into the sewage pipes. Most of the time, all the water passes through the treatment plant and is cleaned. However, when it rains hard for a long time, the sewer pipes can flood. To prevent the water in the pipes from backing up into the streets or breaking the pipes, there is an open section of pipe near the plant. When heavy rains come, the water overflows into the water body before reaching the plant. Because the sewage is mixed with the sewer water, the sewage pours into the waterway without being cleaned. This causes pollution. Cities are now beginning to separate the two systems of pipes. This prevents sewage from mixing with the runoff from the streets.

See also WASTE DISPOSAL.

SEX When a scientist talks about the sex of an organism, he or she is referring to whether the organism is male or female. Generally, male organisms produce sex cells called sperm. Female organisms usually produce sex cells called ova, or eggs (see GAMETE). The male is generally called the father and the female is called the mother.

In some species of organisms, the male and the female differ in appearance. These external differences are a type of polymorphism called sexual dimorphism (see POLYMORPHISM).

Some organisms produce both male and female gametes. These organisms are called hermaphrodites (see HERMAPHRODITE). Some organisms, such as certain fungi, have many "sexes," which are usually called mating types. The sex of an organism is important for reproduction (see REPRODUCTION). In sexual reproduction, a male gamete fertilizes (combines with) a female gamete to produce an embryo (see EMBRYO; FERTILIZATION). The embryo will eventually grow into a fully formed organism. Among some organisms, a female gamete may develop into a fully formed organism without being fertilized. This process is called parthenogenesis (see PARTHENOGENESIS).

A major advantage of sexual reproduction is that it allows the production of new organisms that have some of the characteristics of both parents. This is important in evolution (see EVOLUTION).

Some organisms reproduce asexually, a process in which sex is not involved (see ASEXUAL REPRODUCTION). Asexual reproduction needs only one parent to produce an offspring. All the offspring are identical to the parent.

See also GENETICS; HEREDITY; REPRODUCTIVE SYSTEM.

SEX CHROMOSOMES The sex chromosomes determine the sex of an animal (see CHROMOSOME). Normal body cells in a human being contain 22 pairs of chromosomes and two extra chromosomes, which are called the sex chromosomes. One of these is called the X chromosome and the other is called the Y chromosome. A female has two X chromosomes in her cells. When sex cells, or gametes, are being formed, a female can produce eggs with only X chromosomes, but a male (which has both types of chromosomes) can produce sperm with either an X or a Y chromosome (see GAMETE). When the egg and sperm join during fertilization, they produce a zygote. This zygote can contain either two X chromosomes, and thus produce a female, or one X chromosome and one Y chromosome—in which case it will produce a male (see FERTILIZATION; ZYGOTE). All mammals and birds determine their sex in this manner, although in birds the female has an X and a Y and the male has two X chromosomes. There are no genes on the Y chromosome in humans and most other mammals, but the Y chromosome is necessary to produce maleness.

See also REPRODUCTION; X CHROMOSOME; Y CHROMOSOME.

SEXUALLY TRANSMITTED DISEASE

A sexually transmitted disease (STD) is a disease that is spread by sexual activity, such as sexual intercourse. STDs are caused by a variety of bacteria and viruses. In some cases, an STD results in noticeable symptoms, such as pain or inflammation. In many cases, however, the infected person does not realize that he or she has the disease. However, the STD may be causing damage to internal tissues and organs (see BACTERIA; DISEASE; INFLAMMATION; REPRODUCTION; REPRODUCTIVE SYSTEM; VIRUS).

STDs include Acquired Immune Deficiency Syndrome (AIDS), chlamydia, gonorrhea, herpes simplex type two, and syphilis (see AIDS; GONORRHEA; HERPES; SYPHILIS). STDs have increased in the United States since the 1950s. Chlamydia is the most widespread STD in the United States. Men who have chlamydia may experience a discharge from the penis and a burning sensation while urinating. Women who have chlamydia may experience an unusual vaginal discharge and may develop inflammation in the reproductive organs. Babies born to infected women may be infected themselves. Some STDs, such as chlamydia, gonorrhea, and the early stages of syphilis, can be cured with antibiotics and other drugs (see ANTIBIOTIC; DRUG). Other diseases, such as AIDS and herpes simplex type two, have no known cure. If left untreated, many STDs can cause permanent damage or even death. In addition, an infected person continues spreading the STD for as long as the bacteria or virus is active. This is why it is important that anyone who thinks he or she may be infected with an STD be examined by a doctor as soon as possible.

SHAD A shad is a fish that belongs to the herring family, Clupeidae. There are several species of shad in North America. They generally range from about 10 to 18 in. [25.4 to 45 cm] in length. All shad are silvery fish. Their bodies are very thin from side to side. Most shad live in the ocean but return to freshwater streams to spawn in the spring (see SPAWNING). Some species of shad live in rivers and lakes their entire lives without going to the sea. These shad do not grow as large as those species that do go to sea.

The best-known shad is the American shad. It spends its adult life in the Atlantic Ocean and enters coastal rivers—from Florida to New Brunswick, Canada—to spawn. The American shad is a large fish, sometimes reaching 23 in. [58.4 cm] in length. It is a popular game fish on the east coast of the United States, where it is also a popular food fish.

SHALE Shale is a very fine-grained sedimentary rock (see SEDIMENTARY ROCK). It forms when layers of silt and clay are cemented together (see CLAY; SILT). Shale accounts for about half of the exposed sedimentary rock on the earth's surface. It is made of layers of rock that split easily. Some types of shale are ground up to make bricks and cement. Other types of shale are rich in petroleum.
See also PETROLEUM.

SHALE
Shale is a type of sedimentary rock made up of layers that easily split apart.

SHALLOT A shallot is a perennial herbaceous plant closely related to the onion. It is commonly considered to belong to the lily family, although some botanists now put the onions and their relatives in a separate family called the Alliaceae (see HERBACEOUS PLANT; LILY FAMILY; PERENNIAL PLANT). The shallot has small leaves, which are usually tube-shaped. Its flowers are red or purple and grow in umbels on a 10 in. [25 cm] stalk (see

SHALLOT
Shallots are members of the lily family. They produce flavorful bulbs that are similar to, but smaller than, those of their close relative, the onion.

INFLORESCENCE). The shallot produces a bulb that is smaller than that of the onion (see BULB AND CORM; ONION). As with the onion, the shallot bulb is often used in cooking as a flavoring.

SHARK A shark is a saltwater fish that belongs to the class Chondrichthyes (see FISH). The skeleton of a shark is made up of cartilage rather than bone. There are about 350 species of sharks throughout the world's oceans. Many species are found in the waters off North America.

The dogfish shark grows less than 3.3 ft. [1 m] long. It eats small fish and invertebrates (see INVERTEBRATE). The whale shark—the largest of all fish—can reach about 50 ft. [15 m] in length. It eats mainly plankton (see PLANKTON). Many sharks grow several feet long and eat large fish. These sharks have many razor-sharp teeth. Sharks are often referred to as the "garbage collectors of the seas" because they feed on dead fish and other dead animals on the ocean bottom. Bottles, cans, tires, and boards are also sometimes found in the stomachs of sharks.

A few species of sharks can be dangerous to humans. The white shark, tiger shark, hammerhead shark, and blue shark are all known to have attacked swimmers. However, shark attacks cause relatively few deaths. Most sharks swim away from humans.

See also RAY; SCAVENGER.

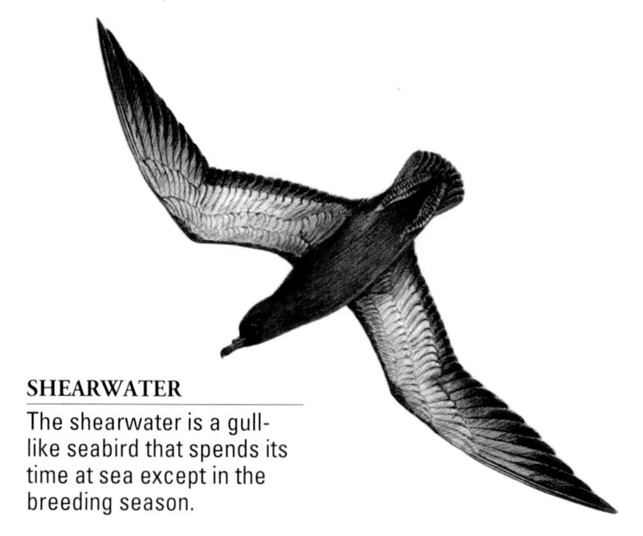

SHEARWATER
The shearwater is a gull-like seabird that spends its time at sea except in the breeding season.

SHEARWATER A shearwater is a seabird that belongs to the family Procellariidae. A shearwater looks like a seagull (see GULL). It has long, narrow wings; dark feathers on its back; and light feathers on its belly. A number of species of shearwaters are found off the coasts of North America.

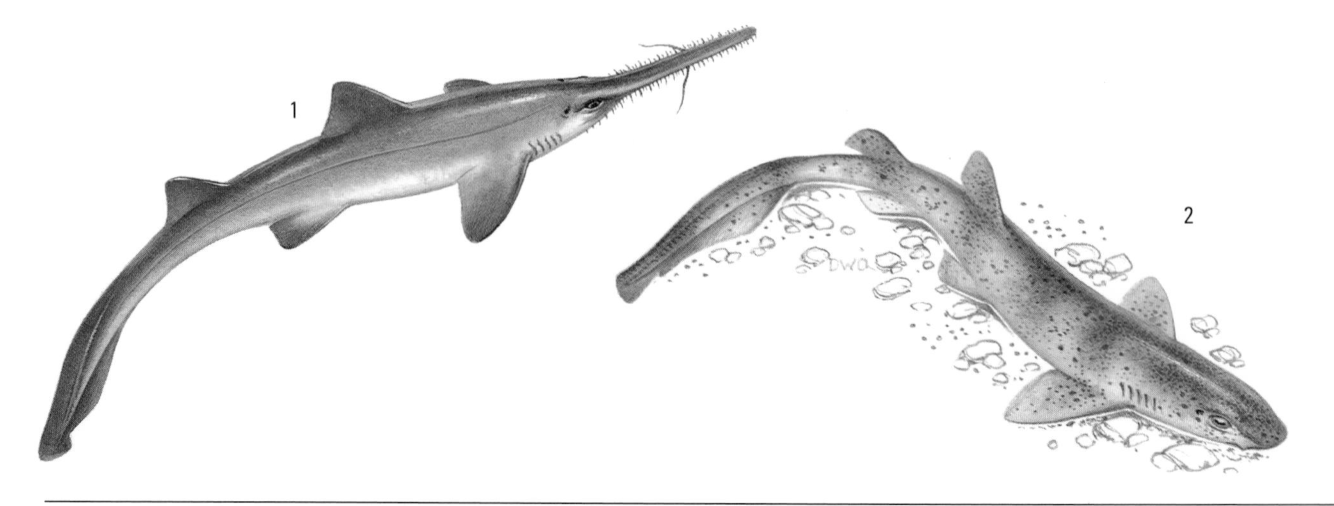

SHARK
Sharks vary widely in shape from (1) the unusual sawshark to (2) the cat shark. All sharks share the characteristic of having a skeleton made of cartilage rather than bone.

Shearwaters come ashore only to lay their eggs. They may fly very long distances to reach their breeding grounds. For the rest of the time shearwaters live out on the sea, often far from land. They eat fish and squid, which they scoop up from the water while they are flying.
See also MIGRATION.

SHEEP Sheep are hoofed mammals belonging to the same family as cattle and goats (see MAMMAL). Sheep probably were first domesticated in southwest Asia more than ten thousand years ago. Today, sheep are one of the commonest of domesticated animals.

Several wild species, such as the argali, urial, and mouflon, are related to domesticated sheep. The argali, which lives in the mountains of central Asia, is the largest of all the wild sheep. The male may stand 4 ft. [1.2 m] tall at the shoulder. The mouflon is the only wild sheep still living in southern Europe.

Domesticated sheep have been slowly and carefully bred (see BREEDING). At first, the wild sheep were tamed for their hides and milk. Soon afterward, they became important for their fleece (wool). Through breeding, the coarse hair that covered the wild sheep was developed into a soft coat of wool. Only in the last two hundred years have breeders bred some sheep primarily for their meat. Domestic sheep vary greatly in size. From the hoof to the shoulder, sheep range from about 2.5 to 4 ft. [0.8 to 1.2 m] in height. They weigh from 100 to 350 lb. [45 to 158 kg]. Sheep fleece can be white, gray, brown, or black. The animals live together in flocks. Sheep are timid animals, usually running away from danger. Both male and female wild sheep have horns for protection, but not all domesticated sheep have horns. In some breeds of domesticated sheep, only the males, called rams, have horns. Female sheep, called ewes, usually bear one or two babies, called lambs, in the spring.

Sheep feed on grass and other small plants. They are cud chewers. This means that a sheep swallows its food and stores it in a division of the stomach called the rumen. The food is partially digested in the rumen and then passed back into the mouth. The sheep then finishes chewing this food, called cud, and swallows it (see RUMINANT).

Sheep are classified into groups depending on their fleece. The three main groups are long wool, medium wool, and fine wool.

Three of the most important long-wooled breeds come from England. They are the Lincoln, Leicester, and Cotswold. Lincoln sheep are popular on ranges in various parts of the world, including Australia, Argentina, and the western United States. This breed is among the largest of domestic sheep. They produce the longest fleece.

Medium-wooled sheep are raised primarily for the meat they produce, but they are also a source of wool. The most important breeds are the Hampshire Down, Shropshire, Southdown, and Suffolk.

Most of the fine-wooled sheep belong to the

SHEEP
Sheep leaving the shearing shed on this Australian sheep station are herded together before being let out to graze. Sheep are raised for their milk, wool, meat, and hides.

SHEEP—Varieties
There are many kinds of wild and domestic sheep. Shown here are (1) the Dalesbred, which produces coarse wool for making tweeds and carpets, (2) the urial, a wild sheep from Asia, seen scratching itself with its horn, (3) the Barbary sheep, whose males have a mane at the throat, and (4) the Mongolian, a fat-tailed sheep from China.

Spanish Merino breed. The Rambouillet, which is also a fine-wool breed, is descended from the Spanish Merino. These two are now the chief wool breeds of the western United States. The Merino also is an important wool breed in the sheep-raising regions of Argentina, Uruguay, South Africa, and Australia. The Rambouillet breed, besides being valued for its wool, is also prized for its meat.

There are two very different ways of raising sheep in the United States. One way is on the range. Sheep are grouped into large herds of one to two thousand. The sheep eat grass in the pasture, and a large herd may move over long distances during the grazing season. The other way of raising sheep is on farms. A farmer raises between thirty and a few hundred sheep. The sheep are kept in fenced pastures. In the winter, the animals are fed grain and hay.

Besides their importance for food and clothing, sheep also supply leather. In addition, the sheep's body provides the raw materials for glue, suet, soap, and fertilizer.

SHELL A shell is the hard outer covering of an egg or animal. The word *shell* is most often used in connection with snails and other mollusks (see MOLLUSCA).

The mollusk shell is formed by the animal's mantle. The mantle is a thick flap of skin surrounding most of the animal's body. Cells in the mantle secrete (give off) calcium carbonate and other materials that make up the shell. Most of the material is secreted at the edge of the mantle. As the animal grows, the mantle edge keeps adding more material to the edge of the shell. As a result, growth lines can clearly be seen on many shells.

There are three main shell layers. The outer layer, the periostracum, consists of a horny material called conchiolin. Periostracum is responsible for nearly all the color of the shell. However, seashells washed up

SHELL

Illustrated above is a selection of mollusk shells. Land, sea, and freshwater mollusks are the most common shelled animals.

on the shore have usually lost most of the periostracum, so they often look dull and have little color. Under the periostracum is the prismatic layer. This layer is made up of columns of calcium carbonate arranged at right angles to the surface of the shell. These columns are separated from each other by narrow columns of conchiolin. The innermost layer of the shell is called the nacreous layer. It is made of thin plates of calcium carbonate alternating with thin plates of conchiolin. The material is very smooth and shiny. It is commonly called mother-of-pearl. While the periostracum and the prismatic layer are usually formed only by the mantle edge, the nacreous layer is secreted by the entire mantle.

People use shells in many different ways. Jewelry and other decorative items are made from shells. Oyster farmers spread dead oyster shells over the floor of the ocean to provide places for newly hatched oysters to attach themselves. Oyster shells are sometimes used for building roads, especially in the Bermuda Islands. Shells have often been used for money throughout history.

SHELLAC Shellac is a resin made from the secretions of the lac insect (see RESIN). These insects are found in India and Myanmar (formerly Burma). They give out a sticky, gummy substance as they feed on the sap from trees (see SCALE INSECT). This substance is called lac.

To make commercial shellac, natural lac is scraped from the trees, washed, melted, and then filtered to remove bits of twig and bark. The lac flakes are yellow, orange, or reddish but can be bleached white. Chemically, shellac is a natural polymer (see POLYMER).

Shellac is used in making many products, such as sealing wax and hair spray. It was once used, along with fine clay, to mold phonograph records. Alcohol solutions of shellac, which are also called shellac, are used as varnish for sealing and finishing wooden furniture and flooring.

See also LACQUER; VARNISH.

SHEPARD, ALAN B., JR. (1923–) Alan Shepard was America's first astronaut in space. Shepard made this first spaceflight aboard the *Freedom 7* on May 5, 1961. Ten years later, in 1971, he commanded the Apollo 14 mission to the moon.

Shepard was born at East Derry, New Hampshire. He graduated from the United States Naval Academy in 1944 and later became a naval test pilot. He had a distinguished career in the U.S. Navy and was a lieutenant commander in the Atlantic Fleet when he was chosen for space service.

See also APOLLO PROJECT; SPACE EXPLORATION.

SHIPS AND SHIPBUILDING

Thousands of years ago, people learned the benefits of carrying themselves and their goods from one place to another by water. Humans developed ships to do this. Early ships were propelled (pushed forward) by oars or sails. Today, most ships are powered by diesel engines or steam turbines that turn propellers. Some warships are powered by nuclear power or gas turbines.

The main classes of ships today are passenger ships; freighters, or cargo ships; container ships; tankers for bulk liquids; fish-processing ships; and warships and patrol ships.

Up until the first half of the twentieth century passenger liners carried people across the oceans of

DEVELOPMENT OF SHIPS

Early boats and ships, from the Egyptian Nile boat to the fast clipper ships, were powered by sail. Some, like the trireme and Viking longship, had oars. Steam began to replace sails with the *Great Britain*. *Turbinia* was the first ship with steam turbine engines. Steamships reached their peak with fast ocean liners, such as the *United States*.

the world, but today most people travel over the oceans in airplanes. However, passenger ships such as car ferries, hovercrafts, and hydrofoils are still widely used to carry people for relatively short distances over water. The larger car ferries cross bodies of water such as the Adriatic and Baltic Seas and the English Channel. The largest ferries carry up to 800 passengers and 300 cars. Those that make overnight crossings have cabins for passengers to sleep in.

Cargo ships are the workhorses of the sea. There are four main groups: general cargo ships, tankers, dry bulk carriers, and multipurpose ships. Freighters carry from 1,000 to 13,000 tons [900 to 11,700 metric tons] of cargo in compartments called holds. Container ships carry large metal containers (rectangular boxes) filled with freight. The containers are stacked on the decks of these specially built ships.

Tankers carry oil, chemicals, and other liquids. When loaded, they float very low in the water. The huge new supertankers carry up to 405,000 tons [450,000 metric tons] of oil. Supertankers can be over 1,500 ft. [457 m] long.

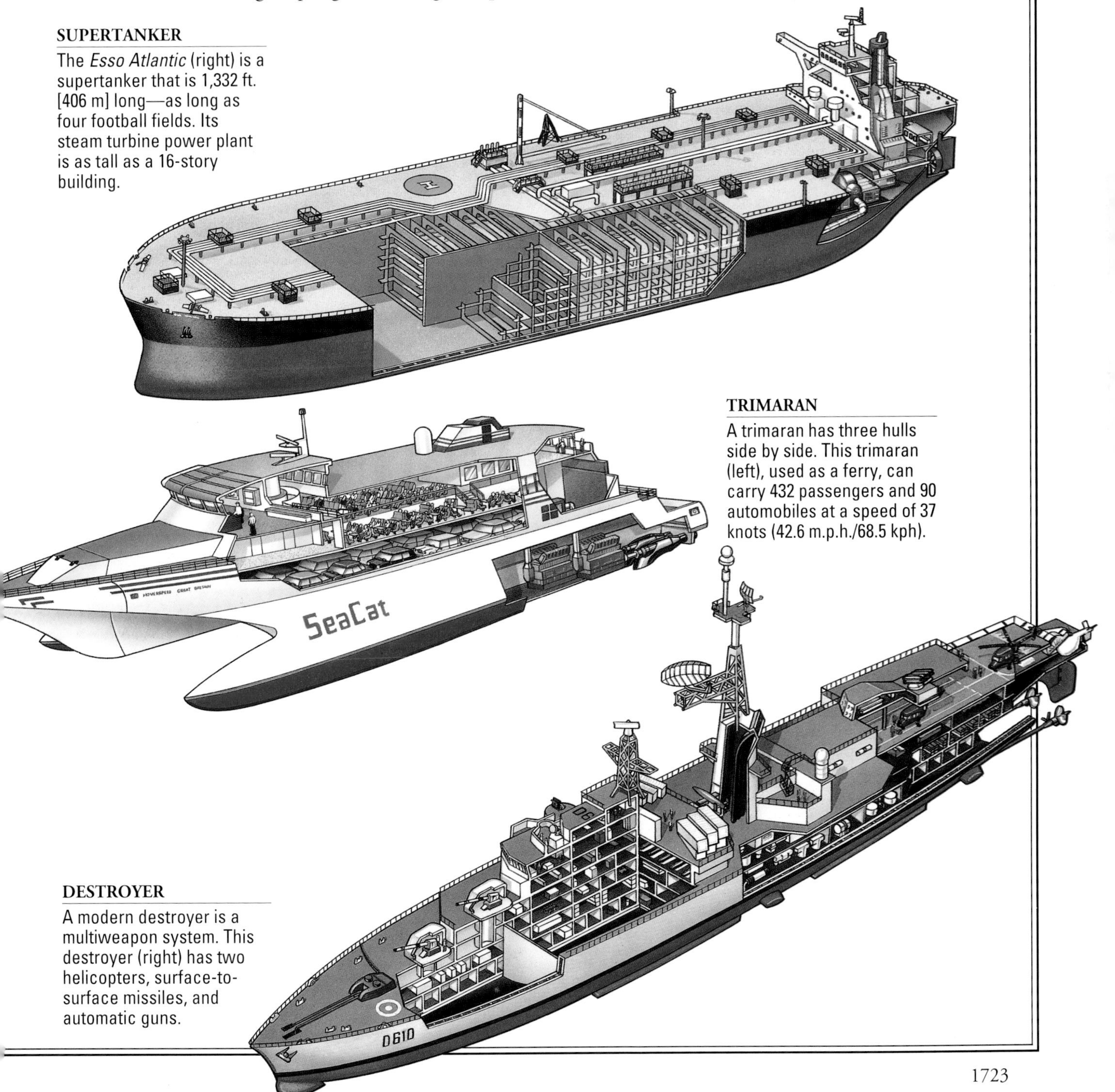

SUPERTANKER

The *Esso Atlantic* (right) is a supertanker that is 1,332 ft. [406 m] long—as long as four football fields. Its steam turbine power plant is as tall as a 16-story building.

TRIMARAN

A trimaran has three hulls side by side. This trimaran (left), used as a ferry, can carry 432 passengers and 90 automobiles at a speed of 37 knots (42.6 m.p.h./68.5 kph).

DESTROYER

A modern destroyer is a multiweapon system. This destroyer (right) has two helicopters, surface-to-surface missiles, and automatic guns.

Oceanographic research ships carry equipment and scientists who look for new mineral deposits under the sea and try to learn more about ocean currents and marine life (see OCEANOGRAPHY). Fish-processing ships are large ships that serve as "mother ships" to large fishing fleets. Smaller ships bring their catches to the "mother ship" for processing and storage. Warships include aircraft carriers, cruisers, destroyers, submarines, and support ships. Most nations with borders on a sea have fleets of warships, as well as smaller coastal patrol ships.

Parts of a ship A ship is one of the most complicated objects made by humans. It must create its own electricity and heat. It carries its own fuel, food, water, and spare parts. The parts of a ship include the hull and superstructure, engine, propellers, and rudder.

The hull is the watertight body of the ship. It is made up of a heavy keel, or backbone; steel ribs, or frames; and large steel outer plates that are connected by rivets or welding. Bulkheads, or walls, divide the hull into compartments. Each

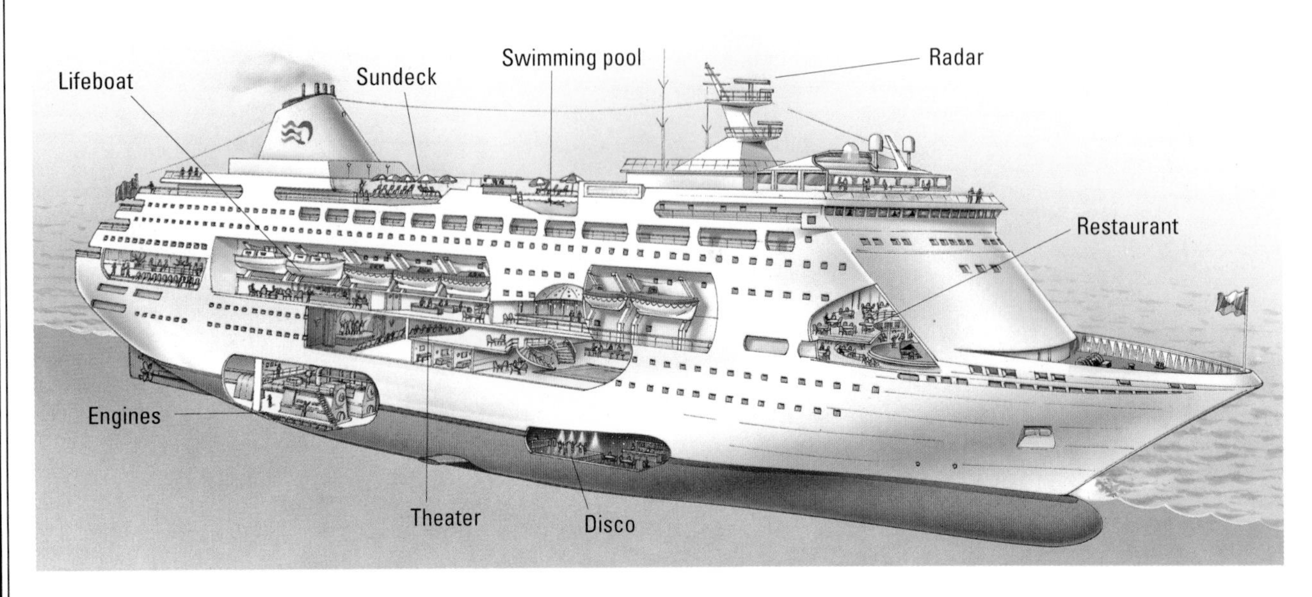

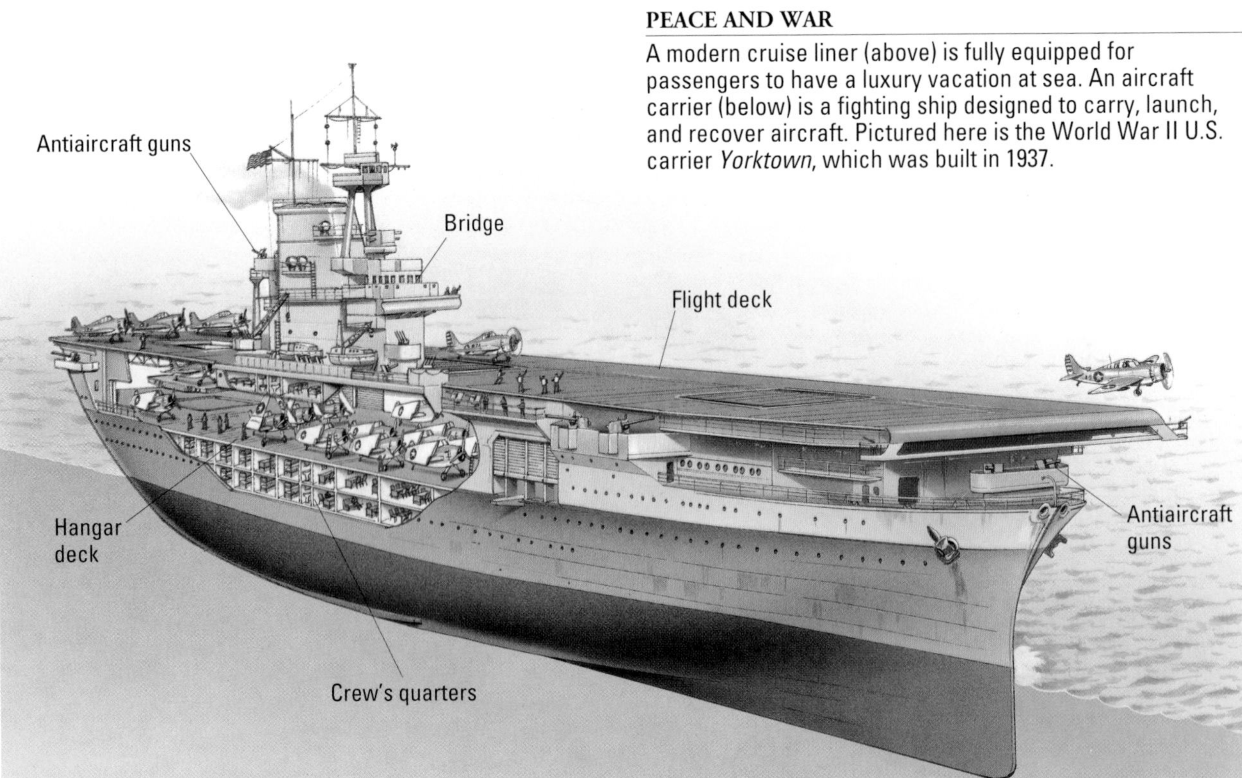

PEACE AND WAR

A modern cruise liner (above) is fully equipped for passengers to have a luxury vacation at sea. An aircraft carrier (below) is a fighting ship designed to carry, launch, and recover aircraft. Pictured here is the World War II U.S. carrier *Yorktown*, which was built in 1937.

compartment has watertight doors so it can be shut off from the next compartment in case of emergency. Each compartment is divided into several decks, or levels. The top of the hull is usually called the main deck. Everything above the main deck is referred to as the superstructure.

Ships float because they weigh less than the water they displace (push aside). However, ships must do more than float. They must also speed through the water. A ship's hull has a pointed bow (front part) that pushes water aside, just as a snowplow pushes snow from its path.

Ships roll from side to side and pitch up and down, from bow to stern (back part), in large ocean waves. Special underwater stabilizing fins lessen these motions. Most ships are driven by diesel or steam turbine engines. Diesel engines cost less to operate than steam engines, but diesel-powered ships are generally slower than steam-powered ships. In steam turbines, steam from a boiler spins a turbine that drives the propeller. On nuclear-powered ships, the nuclear reactor heats water into steam, and the steam spins a turbine. Engineers are working on designs for gas turbines for ships of the future (see DIESEL; ENGINE; GAS TURBINE; NUCLEAR ENERGY; STEAM ENGINE; TURBINE).

Propellers, which are attached to the engine, move a ship through the water. They are attached to long shafts that jut out from the underwater portion of the stern (see PROPELLER).

The rudder is a large steel structure hinged to the stern of the ship. It turns the ship, allowing the pilot to steer. Cables, electric wires, or hydraulic tubes connect the rudder with the ship's steering wheel in the pilot house, or bridge, of the ship (see HYDRAULICS). Ships can also be steered automatically by a device called a gyropilot. If the ship strays from its intended course, a gyrocompass starts an electric motor that turns the steering wheel and moves the ship back on course (see GYROSCOPE).

Shipbuilding Shipbuilding begins with the design and building plans for the ship. The design is worked out by naval architects to agree with a general description given by the person who is buying the ship. Hull models are tested in towing tanks—water-filled troughs that simulate wave conditions in the ocean. Next, the steel parts of the ship are cut to the required shape by automatic burning machines. The various pieces are then brought to a welding shop where flat plates and shapes are assembled, often using automatic welding machines.

In the shipyard these are used to make up huge prefabricated sections of the ship, sometimes complete with wiring and piping. The sections are placed using a crane into a framework called a shipway, where they are welded together to form the ship's hull. After the hull is built, parts of the superstructure are added. The ship is launched, or slid into the water, when it is about 70 to 80 percent complete. Once in the water, it is pulled to an outfitting dock where the superstructure is completed. Before the ship is delivered to its owner, it undergoes tests to make sure that all equipment is in good working order and that the ship performs as it should.

PROJECT 49

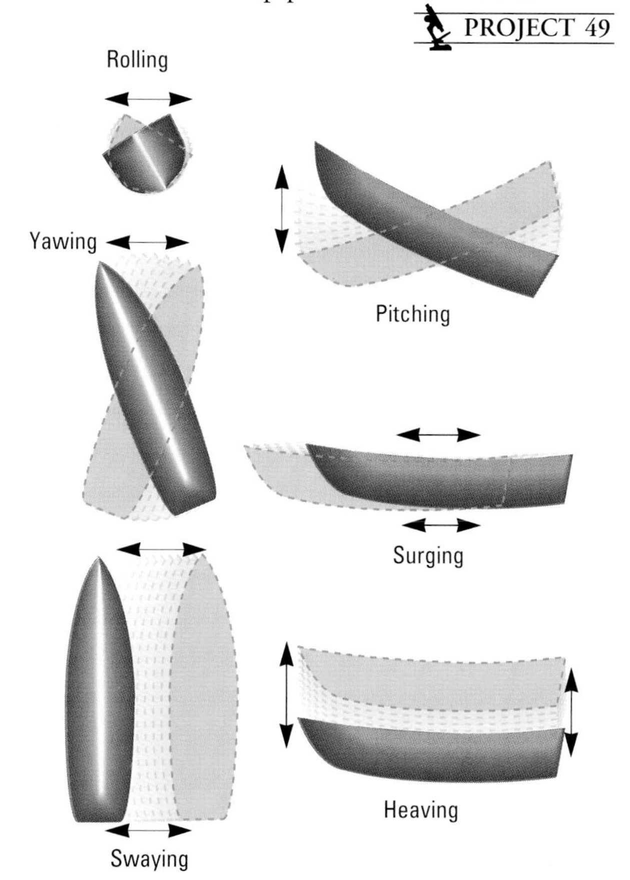

SHIP MOVEMENTS

There are many ways in which the hull of a ship can move in the water, some of which are shown here.

SHOCK Shock is a serious condition in which the major organs of the body do not receive enough blood. Shock may be produced by allergic reactions, serious injuries, or serious infections (see ALLERGY; INFECTION). A person who is in shock has pale, cold, clammy skin and shallow, irregular breathing. He or she also has a weak, rapid pulse and low blood pressure. The person feels weak and may become unconscious. After a serious accident, it may be shock that causes death rather than injury from the accident itself.

The reactions that occur due to shock result from problems with the circulatory system (see CIRCULATORY SYSTEM). Blood vessels dilate (widen), and fluid passes out of the blood into the tissues. Because of this, there is a drop in blood pressure and volume. Shock needs immediate expert medical attention. Useful first aid measures include keeping the patient lying down and warm, stopping any bleeding, and giving artificial respiration if breathing stops.
See also FIRST AID.

SHOCK WAVE A shock wave is a wave of high pressure that forms in gas or liquid as an object moves through it at high speed, or as the gas or liquid flows around the object. Shock waves are also known as pressure waves. For a shock wave to form, the movement of the object or of the fluid (gas or liquid) must be as fast or faster than the speed of sound. The shock waves move away from the object at the speed of sound.

A shock wave is made in the air when a supersonic airplane flies overhead at the speed of sound or faster. When the wave reaches the ground, a sonic boom is heard as the wave strikes the ears.
See also SUPERSONIC FLIGHT.

SHOCK WAVE
The *Concorde* (below) is an airplane that can fly at supersonic speeds (faster than the speed of sound). When a plane flies at subsonic speeds (1), sound waves (shown as circles) travel at the speed of sound and move out in front of the plane. A plane flying at the speed of sound causes sound waves to build up, forming a shock wave. When a plane flies at supersonic speeds (2), it leaves the shock wave behind. When the shock wave hits the ground, it creates a sonic boom.

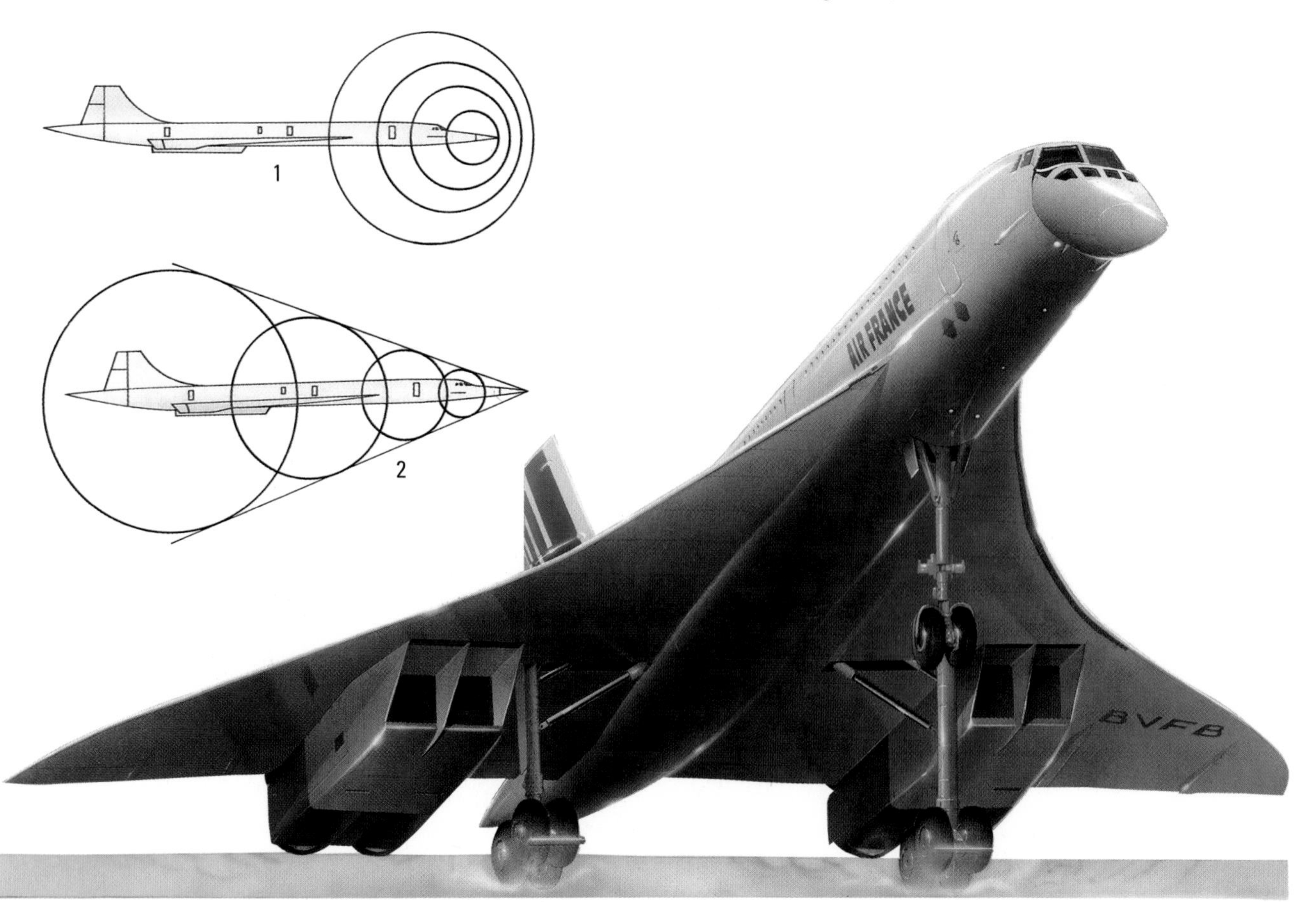

SHREW

Shrews are small, short-lived animals that resemble mice (although they are not rodents). Pictured here are (1) a pygmy white-toothed shrew, (2) a common shrew, and (3) a water shrew.

SHREW Shrews are small mammals that belong to the family Soricidae (see MAMMAL). There are about three hundred species of shrews, found all over the world except in Australia. These mouselike animals have small eyes and ears. They have a long, slender snout that extends over the lower lip. The teeth of many shrews have red tips.

Most species live in grassy or wooded areas, though some live in trees, and a few spend most of their time in water. Most of these animals alternate three hours of activity with three hours of sleep. This cycle continues day and night. When awake, shrews eat almost all the time. Their diet is made up of small invertebrates, such as insects and worms, and plants. Some shrews eat more than their own weight in food every day. Without food, shrews starve to death in a few hours.

Many shrews, such as the musk shrews, have glands that give off a fluid with a very strong odor. These scents protect the shrew, discouraging attack by other animals.

Shrews are sensitive animals and may be killed by the shock of rough handling or loud noises. Their natural enemies include several birds of prey and snakes. Shrews usually live alone, coming together only for mating. After mating and a gestation period of about twenty days, a female gives birth to a litter of two to ten blind, hairless young (see GESTATION PERIOD). The average life span of a shrew is less than two years.

The pygmy white-toothed shrew is one of the smallest living mammals. It is about 1.5 in. [3.5 cm] long and weighs only about 0.07 oz. [2 g]. It lives in southern Europe.

SHRIKE A shrike is a bird that belongs to the family Laniidae. North American shrikes are gray and white with a dark tail, wings, and "mask" over their eyes. There are two species in North America. The northern shrike is found in Canada and the northern United States as well as in Europe, Asia, and Africa. It reaches 8 in. [20 cm] in length. The loggerhead shrike lives in Mexico, the United States, and southern Canada. It grows to 7 in. [17.5 cm] long. Shrikes eat insects and small rodents, which they catch and kill with their sharp, hooked beaks. They often stick their prey on long thorns of trees or on barbs of barbed-wire fences. Then they pick off small pieces of the prey and eat it bit by bit. Shrikes are sometimes called butcher birds in England.

SHRIMP The shrimp is a crustacean and belongs to the phylum Arthropoda (see ARTHROPODA; CRUSTACEAN). It is related to the crab, crayfish, and lobster. However, the shrimp does not have large claws and is much smaller than the lobster.

Shrimp have long feelers and five pairs of delicate legs. To escape quickly, the animals swim backward with fast strokes of their fanlike tails. Strong muscles in the back move the tail. These muscles make the animal's back look "humped," or arched. The

SHRIMP

A cleaner shrimp (above) serves a useful purpose by cleaning fish that have parasites or injuries. The brightly colored mantis shrimp (left) preys on fish and shellfish, which it attacks by shooting out its long front legs.

shrimp's body is covered by a thin, translucent (clear) exoskeleton (see SKELETON). This exoskeleton is jointed, which allows the animal to move easily. As the shrimp grows, it forms a new exoskeleton and sheds the old one (see MOLTING). Some shrimp grow to be 9 in. [22 cm] long. Shrimp live mainly on the seabed and feed on tiny ocean life, including plankton (see PLANKTON).

There are about two thousand species of shrimp. The common American shrimp is found in coastal waters of the Atlantic Ocean. This species may grow as long as 7 in. [18 cm]. The common shrimp spawns early in spring (see SPAWNING). The female lays from about 500,000 to 1,000,000 eggs directly into the water. The eggs drop to the sea bottom and hatch in about twenty-four hours. Most other shrimp species carry their eggs attached to their abdomens. Shrimp go through ten larval (developmental) stages before they reach adulthood (see LARVA; METAMORPHOSIS).

The shrimping industry is one of the most valuable fishing industries in the United States. Shrimp are fished from Alaska and Maine southward along the coasts as far as Argentina.

SHRUB A shrub is a woody plant with several stems, all of which are about the same size (see WOODY PLANT). Most shrubs are less than 10 ft. [3 m] tall. Under the proper conditions, however, some shrubs, such as lilac, may grow as tall as a small tree. A bush is any woody plant with many densely packed branches. It may be a true shrub or a tree that has been cut down and trimmed to shape. Shrubs and bushes are often used to landscape yards and parks.

SHRUB

Shrubs are often planted in parks and gardens for their attractive and sometimes scented flowers. Pictured here are lilac (on the left) and viburnum (right).